*footnote;

A Literary Journal of History

· Various Authors ·

Selected by Eric Shonkwiler and Leah Angstman
Curated and Edited by Leah Angstman

Alternating Current Press
Boulder, Colorado

ISBN-13 (paperback): 978-1-946580-20-7
ISBN-10 (paperback): 1-946580-20-1
ISBN-13 (ebook): 978-1-946580-49-8

Interior and cover design: Leah Angstman

Printed in the United States of America

10 9 8 7 6 5 4 3 2 1

"History is the study
of all the world's crime."
—Voltaire

Letter from the Editor

Leah Angstman

L atc, as usual, but here we are. The fifth issue of our annual literary publication contains 46 works of poetry, fiction, essays, articles, and nonfiction by 41 authors about various historical topics, paired with dozens of photographs. Within these pages, you will find contemporary outlooks on history right alongside little-known public domain works that feel as fresh and as vibrant (and as scary) as if they were written today. Here, the old meets the new, and you'll discover fascinating history from a personal, accessible, nonscholarly literary approach. I'll warn you now that some of the material is heavy, graphic, and uncomfortable, as most of history is.

With our current atmosphere being what it is—uncaring and unjust to so many people—there's an abundance of social justice writing in this issue, showing the cyclical nature of history throughout world wars, American wars, the Civil Rights era, and beyond. We begin with the father of all modern wars, World War II, as we dissect a Nazi octopus, dive into the darkness of the Holocaust, and go through an alternative history of wartime medical experiments and the polio vaccine.

Girls face mistreatment as "comfort women" in Indonesia, hostages in Budapest, and massacre victims of U.S. violence in Korea. We travel through Siberia with the Czechoslovak Legion, flee with refugees, and hold our breath through 1960s protests, lynchings, and the race-related hate crimes of the American Civil Rights movement. From the Orangeburg massacre to the Freedom Summer murders, we meet the lives lost tragically by racists, and round out the 60s with voices from the Memphis Sanitation Workers Strike and anti-apartheid demonstrations in South Africa.

Nigerian bishop Samuel Ajayi Crowther talks about his time in bondage, which leads us into the horrors of slavery during the American Civil War, where we meet plenty of unsavory characters getting away with awful crimes—among them the Confederates of Thomas' Legion—and a few sparks of hope and kindness circling the gloom. Follow Civil War troops into Florida, North Carolina, Georgetown, and Virginia, and spend time with Dr. Mary Edwards Walker and other nurses and surgeons who administered to fallen soldiers. Women face adversity with their passions and skills in a stiff patriarchy, and we watch female doctors, laborers, immigrants, and even Mozart's sister succeed among the difficulty or fail with sorrow at the whims of powerful men.

Immigrants tell their stories of the Lower East Side and Thanksgiving Day parades, and historical LGBTQ+ stories are told through Henry David Thoreau, Aphra Behn, and the gutting mass-removal of government employees during the Lavender Scare. We visit 1700s witch hunts, ride unicorns through Medieval tapestries, and get goosebumps from featured writer Kathryn Smith's take on the Spiritual movement, where P. T. Barnum, the Fox Sisters, and Sir Arthur Conan Doyle all weigh in about mediums and communing with the dead. Utopian societies and Shaker villages aren't all they're cracked up to be, and hummingbirds during the Luminist period make way for dog-headed human beasts from 16th-century conquistador nightmares and illnesses of everyone from George Washington's brother to chain-smoking miners of 19th-century Australia.

As always, it's intense. We hope you laugh a little, reflect a little, squirm a little, and enjoy a lot.

Sincerely,
Leah Angstman

Table of Contents

Fiction

The Wehrmachtopus • Gareth Hipwell • 15

The Cure • Morgan Jeffery & Chris Helgens • 24

Secrets • P. D. R. Lindsay • 37

Stand-By • Stuart Stromin • 70

Jubilo Done Pass • Jeremy Ray Jewell • 87

Georgetown Girls • Eneida P. Alcalde • 120

Hopes • Caitlin Mariah • 152

Two Truths and a Lie • Myrlin A. Hermes • 166

A Walk to Lafayette • J. W. Stewart • 173

The Notary's Conquest (A Fragment) • Deva Eveland • 215

Beginnings Emerge Out of Endings and the Like • D. Seth Horton • 226

The Smoker's Lot • Gareth Hipwell • 228

Nonfiction

A Confession of Conspiracy • Horace Doyle Barnette • 63

How I Was Captured into Slavery • Samuel Ajayi Crowther • 82

The Untold Story of the 2nd North Carolina Mounted Infantry • Patrick Barton • 104

The Case of Grace Sherwood • Princess Anne County Court • 187

An Excerpt from *The History of Spiritualism* • Arthur Conan Doyle • 203

Poetry

The Train • Anique Sara Taylor • 34

The Birthday Party, 1944 • Clare Chu • 47

Army without a Country • Johannah Racz Knudson • 48

The Girl from No Gun Ri • Esther Ra • 49

The Death of History • Jahman Hill • 56

Mississippi Buried • Jonathan Andrew Pérez • 60

selective recall • henry 7. reneau, jr. • 68

For Samuel Ajayi Crowther • Ayokunle Falomo • 80

Woman of Breasts • Mary Jane Panke • 86

Death of Colonel Baker (Song from the Civil War) • William Sutherland • 140

Dr. Mary Edwards Walker Counts the Union Dead • Barbara Alvarado • 142

The Explosion at the Arsenal • Jamie Todd Hamilton • 143

Salzburg, Austria, 1773 • Amanda Hodes • 148

Cardinal Virtues • Gretchen Rockwell • 149

Thanksgiving Day Parade, 1929 • Eric Pierzchala • 160

And Yet You Do Not Vote *(Henry David Thoreau)* • Marion Avrilyn Jones • 163

Sympathy • Henry David Thoreau • 164
The Dream • Aphra Behn • 172
After the Hostile Takeover, 1990 • Laura Budofsky Wisniewski • 184
Lynnhaven River, 1706 • Chelsea Bunn • 185
No Locks • Bob Sykora • 208
At New Lebanon They Danced like Ghosts • Bob Sykora • 209
The Hummingbird Artist Dreams of the Ladder of Heaven • Greg Rappleye • 211
The Tribe of Men • Daryl Scroggins • 225

Featured Writer: Kathryn Smith

Considering "the Public Appears Disposed to Being Amused Even When
    They Are Conscious of Being Deceived" (P. T. Barnum, 1855) • 193
The Fox Sisters Hold a Séance • 195
Maggie Fox Speaks to the Dead Girl, Then Is Asked to Remove Her Clothes • 197
The Examination • 198
Animal Magnetism vs. Spiritual Magnetism, or the Vertiginous Sister
    Attempts a Mesmeric State in Order to More Fully Understand • 200

Images

Ukrainian *Ostarbeiter* under German forced labor, 1941 • 23
Dr. Josef Mengele, 1944 • 32
President Franklin Delano Roosevelt, 1933 • 32
Block 10 medical building at Auschwitz, 2008 • 33
Child survivors of Auschwitz in adult clothes, 1945 • 33
Liberated Holocaust train from Bergen-Belsen, 1945 • 35
Cattle car used to deport Slovak Jews, 2017 • 36
Cattle wagon used to transport Belgian Jews, 2007 • 36
Indonesian comfort women, between 1931 and 1945 • 45
Korean comfort girls rescued in Burma, 1944 • 46
Chinese and Malayan comfort girls, c. 1945 • 46
Korean refugees fleeing from the North Korean army, c. mid-1950 • 53
John J. Muccio's memo about No Gun Ri, 1950 • 54
Bullet-riddled No Gun Ri bridge, 2015 • 54
Twin-underpass railroad bridge at No Gun Ri, 1960 • 55
Colonel Turner C. Rogers' memo about No Gun Ri, 1950 • 55
All-Star Bowling Lane in Orangeburg, South Carolina, 2015 • 58
(*GRAPHIC) Orangeburg Massacre by police officers, 1968 • 59
Delano Middleton, Samuel Hammond, Jr., and Henry Smith, 1968 • 59
FBI missing-persons poster for Goodman, Chaney, and Schwerner, 1964 • 61
(*GRAPHIC) Remains of Goodman, Chaney, and Schwerner, 1964 • 62
Freedom Summer Murders historical marker, 2012 • 62
Memphis sanitation workers with "I Am a Man" signs, 1968 • 69
Mounted policemen in South Africa, 2014 • 79

Barefoot policemen in South Africa, 1890 • 79
Samuel Ajayi Crowther, c. 1888 • 81
Freetown, Sierra Leone, mid-19th century • 85
Civil War fight in Volusia County, Florida, 1865 • 103
Cherokee Confederates of Thomas' Legion, 1903 • 119
Colonel George Kirk, c. 1870 • 119
Death of Colonel Edward Baker at Ball's Bluff, 1865 • 139
Battle of Ball's Bluff at the edge of the Potomac, 1861 • 139
Colonel Edward Dickinson Baker, c. 1861 • 141
Dr. Mary Edwards Walker, c. mid-1860s to 1890s • 142
Monument for the Washington Arsenal explosion, c. 1913 • 146
Washington Arsenal women before explosion, c. 1863-1864 • 147
Washington Arsenal explosion debris, 1864 • 147
Maria Anna Mozart, c. 1785 • 148
The Virgin and Unicorn, painting, c. 1602 • 150
The Lady and the Unicorn, painting, late 16th century • 150
The Unicorn Surrenders to a Maiden, tapestry, c. 1495-1505 • 151
The Lady and the Unicorn: Sight, tapestry, c. 1484 to 1500 • 151
Russian immigrant workers, 1909 • 158
Russian immigrant woman sewing, c. 1880-1889 • 159
Russian immigrant woman reclining, 1885 • 159
Russian immigrant woman in chair, c. 1908 • 159
Felix the Cat Thanksgiving Day parade balloon, 1927 • 162
Henry David Thoreau, 1861 • 165
The Rover play script by Aphra Behn, 2023 • 171
Aphra Behn engraving, c. 1680 • 172
Lavender Scare newspaper headline, c. 1950s • 183
Frank Kameny leading LGBTQ+ protest, 1965 • 183
Ducking punishment engraving, 17th-century • 186
Kathryn Smith, 2019 • 192
Ernestine de Faiber and Phineas T. Barnum, c. 1860-70 • 194
P. T. Barnum, 1851 • 194
The Fox sisters lithograph, 1852 • 196
False shoe tips for a medium, 1907 • 199
Medium Eusapia demonstrates how to free her hand, 1907 • 199
Maggie and Kate Fox, 1852 • 202
Séance at Baron von Erhardt's, c. between 1898 and 1920s • 202
Photo of Sir Arthur Conan Doyle with Spirit, 1922 • 205
The spirit of the late Arthur Conan Doyle, 1931 • 206
William Hope, 1950 • 207
Rev. Charles L. Tweedale, Mrs. Tweedale, and a spirit, 1919 • 207
Nashoba Community, 1827 • 208
Shakers' Dance, 1857 • 210

Shakers dancing, 1870 • 210
Passion Flowers and Hummingbirds, painting, c. 1870-83 • 213
Martin Johnson Heade, c. 1870 • 213
Two Hummingbirds with Their Young, painting, c. 1865 • 214
Man with a dog head from *The Nuremberg Chronicle*, 1493 • 224
Lawrence Washington engraving, c. 1738 • 227
Remains of 1850s Kiandra general store, Australia, 2007 • 242

2019 Charter Oak Award Winners & Finalists

First Place • 185
Second Place • 149
Third Place • 49
Finalists • 34, 56, 80, 87, 143, 184, 209, 215, 226

Matter

Letter from the Editor • Leah Angstman • 7
Table of Contents • 9
Featured Writer: Kathryn Smith • 192
Author Biographies • 245
2019 Charter Oak Award • 251
Acknowledgments • 253
Bibliographies & Endnotes • 255
Colophon & Permissions • 259

The Wehrmachtopus

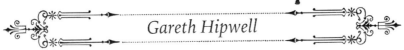

Gareth Hipwell

To consider the creature in its enclosure at the Aquarium du Québec, Sainte-Foy—jewel in the crown of the Société des établissements de plein air du Québec—one could not be sure if it were the Nazi who had absorbed the octopus, or the octopus the Nazi. Logically, of course, there existed the third possibility (in which questions of absorption did not factor), that the so-called *Wehrmachtopus* was the product of a radical morphological mutation in a common- or garden-Nazi that had given rise to something closely resembling an adult *Octopus vulgaris*. Though many in the marine sciences strenuously denied the plausibility of this "Nazi-Octopus Mutation Theory" as advanced, it remained yet the focus of some serious, albeit discreet, inquiry.

While undeniably contentious, the Nazi-to-octopus mutation narrative did not mark the outer limit of the debate. It being axiomatic in the sciences that, if one cannot be right, the surest way to find traction in any field is to be radical, a small but dedicated school had attached itself to a fourth explanation. Although regarded by mainstream biology as little more than a doomed, pseudoscientific putsch prosecuted by a handful of apostates and cryptozoologists, this "Fourth Way" had attracted considerable interest from groups outside the world of marine research. The hypothesis found its clearest expression in a single paper published in the periodical journal *Radical Cephalopolitics*. The article, entitled "Mollusca SS: On an Instance of Auto-Nazification in a North-Atlantic Octopus," had been met in most quarters with a flurry of indignation. The theory posited by the paper's authors—and zealously promulgated by their Fourth Way colleagues besides—held that a center-right-leaning *O. vulgaris*, dissatisfied with the state of play in the Atlantic Northwest and finding itself pushed to the radical, fascist fringe, had voluntarily adopted a suite of *Nationalsozialistische* traits and characteristics. The suggestion that a Common Octopus might elect to transform itself into a Nazi was, of course, wildly out of step with most accepted knowledge of the species. *O. vulgaris* was almost universally acknowledged for a politically liberal and racially tolerant species—the same being broadly true of all the Octopodidae.

Even as the scientists sought to steer their own increasingly heated debate through the labyrinth of peer-review, historians called in to observe the creature jostled to elucidate possible scenarios of their own. Perhaps, some suggested, the Wehrmachtopus was the avatar of an ill-fated Nazi soldier—for a soldier it had undoubtedly been—stationed in East Prussia or the Polish Corridor during the closing stages of the war. Finding himself trapped aboard a stricken transport ship torpedoed by Soviet submarines during the evacuations of Operation Hannibal, the theory ran, as the freezing waters of the Baltic rose about his ankles, would it not have been reasonable for the doomed man to shed his simple soldier's skin and to adopt instead the form of an octopus? Other experts speculated that the unhappy *Mannschaft*, loyal to the Reich unto the end and despairing at the collapse of German forces in the face of the Red Army advance, had thrown himself headlong into the Black Sea, being there commingled with a sympathetic local cephalopod.

Whatever its origins, there could be no denying the creature's political leanings. Within a week of its arrival in Québec, the Wehrmachtopus had taken to arranging the empty cockleshells that collected on the floor of its tank into the shape of what appeared to be crude swastikas. Under questioning by aquarium staff, the creature had itself been invited to confirm the nature of the design with the assistance of a submersible microphone. Amid the confusion of bestial croaks and grindings picked up by the receiver, one among the researchers purported to comprehend a single word, once uttered: "*Hakenkreuz.*" This putative vocalization on the creature's part had since become a source of ongoing scholarly contention in its own right, being much debated in the literature surrounding *O. wehrmachtii.* The accuracy with which the creature was able to reproduce its cockleshell design had only improved with time.

The Third Reich being remembered, among other things, for

its abiding love of uniform and insignia, there were naturally several indications of the Wehrmachtopus' more specific designations within the broad church of Nazism. Double-barred collar *Litzen* at either side of the creature's throat confirmed its enlistment in the German regular army, while pigmentation in the shape of a banded triangular chevron fixed its rank at *Obergefreiter*. The profile of the creature's bottle-green mantle bore a striking resemblance to the shape of the *Stahlhelm*, while two of its eight legs terminated, severally, in a jackboot. Subsequent to its arrival at the aquarium, an inquiry had found that the trawler crew responsible for hauling the creature from the steel-gray waters of a North-Atlantic sound had —desiring souvenirs of their find—relieved the creature of its Luger P08 service pistol and *Wehrmachtsadler* Breast Eagle. These items had yet to be recovered.

On the strength of the evidence elucidated above, and appreciating all too readily the profound historical irony of the creature's form, the Wiesenthal Center had classified the Wehrmachtopus a "Living Symbol of the Horror and Grotesquerie of National Socialism and the Excesses of the Third Reich."

Yet, for all its objectionable trim and trappings, the Wehrmachtopus had fast become the Aquarium du Québec's most lucrative permanent attraction. Installed in a spacious tank, it was exhibited to the public year-round under the masthead *Tentacles of Fascism*. A leading Toronto-based copywriting firm commissioned by the Société had devised the title, along with the accompanying suite of radio and television advertisements. *Don't be a sucker,* urged the campaign, *kommen und sehen die Wehrmachtopus!* The effectiveness of these exhortations was hard to deny. Having enjoyed an initial spike in ticket-takings following the Wehrmachtopus' arrival in Québec, the aquarium had seen sustained month-on-month growth in revenues since the commencement of the advertising push. A character closely modeled on the Wehrmachtopus had even made a guest appearance on *Spongebob Squarepants*.

Today, the Wehrmachtopus attends to its regular morning drills, trailing up and down its tank in a burlesque, eight-legged parody of a goosestep. Children press their faces to the glass, marveling at this strange sea monster that marches and wears boots. A young mother scrambles to dissuade her child from offering his most enthusiastic *Hitlergruß* salute to the enclosure, in imitation of the creature's stance as depicted in the gaudy mural above its tank. On the far side of the aquarium, a sealion bellows at its keeper in a guttural New England accent. Spilled seawater evaporates slowly from the gangways that crisscross the park.

With a creeping slowness that would be incongruous in any other setting, an elderly man wades through a sea of ice-cream smiles and budding sunburns. His clothes, though drab, are well cut; the jacket brings such elegance as it can to the curve of his spine. He is overdressed for the day. Pausing now and then to permit the passage of a skittering child, the old man moves with clear purpose toward the lair of the Wehrmachtopus. Selecting a poolside position at some remove from the densest knot of onlookers, he grips the edge of the tank for support with both hands and presses his knees against the glass. The old man gazes out across the harbor. The light of the summer sun tries in vain to plumb the deep creases that line his face.

A tinny horn sounds above the noise of the crowd, startling the gulls. The dolphin show is about to start. Parents usher their children toward the porpoise pool, maneuvering prams around the warm, salt-rimmed puddles of the concourse. Very soon, the old man is alone beside the big, round tank. Stretched taut against the sky above him, a calico banner offers up a warning in imposing *Fraktur* lettering: *Beware the Tentacles of Fascism.* Excited squeals carry across the water from the far side of the park.

Near the center of its enclosure, the Wehrmachtopus ceases in its parading. Very slowly, it trails across the floor of its enclosure toward the old man, as though drawn along on a fine, braided line. It stops several feet short of the tank's rim. The creature ascends to the level of the air with a gentle, billowing motion. The crown of its head, crosshatched with scars, breaks the surface tension without a sound.

"I had not imagined you could be so small, Herr Octopus," says the old man.

The creature lifts an eye out of the water and blinks against the brightness of the sun.

"In the advertisements, you are like the kraken. They would have you capsizing a dinghy."

Though a citizen of Canada—a nation to which he has belonged both bodily and at law for more than forty years—the old man does not speak as a Canadian. Nor, however, does his speech bear out the rhythms and counterrhythms of his native tongues with any particularity. He speaks as the aurochs might among domestic cattle.

"If they call you *monster*, though, it is only in fun."

The Wehrmachtopus descends to the floor of its tank. Temperate currents fan the creature's arms against the gray cement bottom.

"I think this is very strange." The old man retrieves a faded blue handkerchief from a jacket pocket and draws it across the tip of his bloated nose. He regards the soiled fabric a moment. "For these people, you are either a Nazi who has became as an octopus, or an octopus who is now a Nazi. Where is the difference in this?"

The creature propels itself to the surface of the tank on a jet of water and grimaces at the old man with its hooked, brown beak.

"Yet, they keep you here, feed you, clean your tank when it is dirty. Families visit this place only to look at you. They smile to see you—the children smile."

A solitary gull, its left leg amputated below the knee by some misfortune, caws mirthfully.

"It is best you remain in the water."

Warbling with shrill abandon, a couple of knock-kneed girls appear on the boardwalk and canter past at a gangling tilt. The old man feels suddenly hot. His jacket traps both the warmth of the day and another, more shameful, flush of heat. He glances furtively over his shoulder. Red-faced, the old man turns away from the tank and struggles to catch his breath. The creature, meanwhile, drifts closer to the edge of its enclosure. It retrieves a slick black mussel from the wire basket affixed to the rim of its tank, pries open the shell with pneumatic limbs, and draws the helpless, soft-bodied mollusk into its mouth. The Wehrmachtopus fixes an eye on its elderly visitor. A collective gasp of amazement issues from the stands of the porpoise pool. The old man recovers his wind and turns to address the creature.

"I have been too long with brick-dust and paint and insulation fibers," he wheezes, and retches into his handkerchief. "Of all the things I have been, everything that I have done, I have been a builder most of all. My lungs are proof of this." The old man leans over the side of the tank. Light refracted from the water's surface plays about his forehead. "It is quite simple to be both a Nazi and an octopus, I think," he wheezes.

The creature reaches for another mussel.

"For others, though, to be also a Nazi is not so simple."

The silken skin of the Wehrmachtopus' limbs breaks the taut surface of the water in a dozen places at once. Its arms are suspended momentarily by the salt-density of the solution before sinking once again. The creature keeps the crown of its head perpetually above the water.

"There is a judge in Ottawa—he is in the federal court there—whose name is Noël." The old man snickers without humor. "Is this a name for a judge?"

A faint tremor runs through the Wehrmachtopus' body, retarding its deep-green color momentarily to a mottled gray.

"When these men came to my home—one of them a police detective—when they sat me down beside my wife and began to ask me questions, about Ukraine, about Russia, about Germany, I said to them in a small voice, *like this,* 'Please, officers, you must excuse me a moment—I would like to call my lawyer.' Still they told me I did not need a lawyer. But the more they ask, the more I recognize the need for the lawyer. But, an old man, I did not complain about the unfairness of this. I worried what their response might be."

Something like a bark issues from the creature's mouth. The old man gives a sad smile, as though remembering a faithful dog now long-since dead and buried.

"In the country of my birth, for two hundred years, my family was set apart. We were Germans in a land of Slavs. For a long time, there was nothing so wrong in this. No teasing, no harsh words.

This much my grandmother recalled to me. But still we were *Volks-deutsche*—German, yet somehow not quite German."

A single, piercing blue eye meets the old man's gaze with an arresting serenity.

"The Soviets, though, treated us very badly. When war broke out between Hitler and Stalin, the Russians imprisoned us—I, my mother, sister, grandmother. In this concentration camp, we were only German." The old man frowns. So lined is his face that the expression registers only in a darkening of the shadows around his eyes. "After the war, when I fled the East, in Germany I found I was now a Russian."

On the opposite side of the enclosure, a stray penguin perches at the edge of the Wehrmachtopus' tank. It has escaped, somehow, from its own cold habitat of stone and damp cement. Hesitating a moment—whether nervous of the water or of that which lies beneath it—the little bird leans forward to regard the rippling surface of the tank, and plunges in. A wide octopus eye swivels in what passes for a socket. The creature bunches its limbs into the shape of a steady flame and torpedoes across the tank. By means and method unseen by the old man, the Wehrmachtopus ejects the penguin from its lair and glides with self-satisfied silkiness back toward its elderly visitor.

"I have heard you have the red blood of a man, and not the blue blood of an octopus," the old man remarks. "At one time, they would have called you *Reichsgolem*—something like this. *Not a dumb thing of clay*, they would have said, but something better. An Aryan soldier fashioned from the body of a crafty octopus, the greatest of all nature's imposters."

A juvenile seagull waddles along the gangway beside the tank. Its plumage is still gray and downy at the shoulders, the beak a pale yellow.

"I was very young when my father died," the old man continues. "My grandmother already was living with us then. When the *Schutzstaffel* arrived in Ukraine, I was working to bring in the harvest, mending roofs, whatever employment I could find. Always the wages were very poor. Because I was a German and spoke also Russian, the SS men summoned me to the town hall. My mother was fearful—afraid what would happen if I refused them. So I went. These men ordered me to come with them as an interpreter. Also afraid, I went as I was told. This is the only thing I can do."

With measured solemnity, the creature blinks its approval.

"Is this service?" the old man asks. "Is this not servitude? It is only fear—for myself, and for my family. And yet it is the service of evil they charge me with." With slender fingers the old man grips the edge of the tank. His knuckles whiten, though the skin is already stretched thin over the bones of his hands. "Now these people throw words of condemnation at me in broken German—I, whom they accuse of being an interpreter of murderers. *Sicherheitspolizei, Einsatzkommando, Sicherheitsdienst.* But they mean to say the same thing."

A hearty cheer lifts from the stands of the porpoise pool.

"I remember only peeling potatoes, polishing boots. How can I see these things, in the villages, in the countryside? I did not even have a rifle of my own." The old man paws distractedly at the bulb of his nose. "What are these things you have seen, Herr Octopus, that make you to hide beneath the sea?" he asks. The weight of memory settles heavy on the old man. "I saw many towns along the way," he recalls. "These are places I know I have visited, but whose names I never learned. At this time, the Russians did not erect signs to identify their towns, and I had no map. Without these names to hold them, my memories are in pieces. Together, they add up always to the same place. Maybe it is made of real streets, this town, and of real buildings. But some have stuck in my mind from films I have seen, and from photographs I have been shown. In this town, I know no one outside the barracks. Even there, the names and faces are confused. This place is filled with people I cannot have known. It is only now I have the sensation something is happening just outside the limits of the town. This is how I recall that time."

Oily bubbles issue from the creature's beak in a slow trickle. They roll over shallow wavelets, trailing along the surface of the water before bursting.

"Whatever I once knew, my memories are no longer my own," the old man reflects sadly. "Too many fingers now have smudged them. Yet in these things I do not remember, too, they find accusations."

Like a static hiss, the sound of clapping carries over to the Wehrmachtopus' enclosure. The old man sinks further into his hunch, as though his bent frame remembers suddenly the weight of a rifle. Shortly, children and their parents file away from the porpoise pool two-by-two, chattering and laughing gleefully in the penetrating light of the sun.

"To be both a Canadian and a Nazi—I think now maybe this is impossible," the old man says, his voice wavering. Atop his head, fine strands of milk-white hair flail in the breeze. "I do not remember now if I was always nervous of crowds and crowded places, as my grandmother was."

"*For the monster, perfecting the disguise is a question of immersion,*" the Wehrmachtopus croaks in clipped *Mitteldeutsch*. Beneath the gentle ripples of the water's surface, the creature snaps the heels of its boots together soundlessly. It holds an arm outstretched above the tank in a dripping salute. "*It would be better we not meet again,*" it says. "*I gave up the soil for the sea that I might escape reflection. Your eyes alone are detestable to me.*"

Learn more about German forced labor in the Soviet Union.

Learn more about German mistreatment of Soviet Union POWs.

A Ukrainian *Ostarbeiter* ("Eastern worker") works at the lathe under German forced labor, 1941.

The Cure

Morgan Jeffery & Chris Helgens

An alternative history.

A courier descended the steps and handed Oberman a sheet of parchment encrypted with a secret message. Oberman had an eidetic memory and had long ago memorized the key. This was one reason he'd been chosen to work for the CIA, a new intelligence agency created to try criminals in the wake of the war. Oberman compared the coded message to the key in his mind's eye, rearranging the symbols and letters until they became the names of the men he was now assigned: Dr. Josef Mengele and his team—among them, brain surgeon Hans Shmelzer.

"I'm scared, Daddy," Clara whispered, pulling the blankets over her paralyzed legs.

Hans was, too. There was no room for the disabled in Hitler's superior race. Hans held Clara's hands in his—strong, steady. "Clara, it does no good to be scared," he said. "Obstacles do not exist to be surrendered to."

". . . Only to be broken," they said together.

Clara knew the quote well but not its origins. Hans touched the copy of *Mein Kampf* in his coat pocket and kissed his eight-year-old daughter's forehead. He stood, pausing to turn out the lights.

"Daddy? When can I go back to school?"

Hans sighed. She was a bright girl, hungry to learn. "Be strong, Little Bell. You won't have to hide much longer." Clara wore a mask of strength—but Hans could see the pain in her eyes.

"I love you, Daddy," she said, her tiny voice tinkling like bells. She closed her eyes.

Hans closed the door.

Agent Oberman touched his earpiece, listening. The microphones he'd installed picked up every sound. Aside from the tapping of rain on glass, the girl's bedroom was silent. She was good at being quiet.

Downstairs, Mila sat at the table, smoking. The silk of her nightgown clung to her. She was pencil thin, but her protruding hips gave the illusion of curves. "I'm worried."

She repeated these words daily now. When Clara coughed, cried, or went to sleep after her bedtime story—which was usually read twice. Hans never did the voices right the first time, so he could spend a few more minutes with his daughter.

"No need to be afraid," Hans lied. "She's strong." He set the coffee brewing and massaged his wife's shoulders.

"It's not that. They're saying Americans crossed the Rhine today. Do you understand what it could mean for us if the Reich is found out? Your work with Mengele? It's genocide!" Exasperated, Mila leaned into Hans' touch and took a long drag on her cigarette. She exhaled slowly, the smoke lingering for a moment before dissolving in air. The tension in her shoulders remained.

"It won't come to that," Hans said.

"Why not?" Mila shrugged his hands away and turned to face him, fear in her eyes. "You're putting us in danger supporting a cause I can't even wrap my mind around."

"I'm doing it for her—not the Nazis. You know that."

"You're going to get her killed!"

"She's going to be killed by that virus if I don't do something!" Hans shouted.

"Would you be quiet?" Mila whispered through gritted teeth. "Do you think she can't hear you?"

Hans knelt, cradling her shaking hands in her lap. "I'm so close to finding the cure," he said, lowering his voice.

"I know, but I've heard that before. If we escape, they can't take her."

"If we leave now, the virus will take her. We can hide from the Nazis but not polio."

Agent Oberman took note.

Hans stood over the operating table, stitching together the heads of twins—fusing blood cells and brain stems—Mengele's orders. Surgeries had never made Hans squirm, but today, the smell of iron and formaldehyde twisted his gut. He snipped the final thread. The girls opened their eyes, struggling to breathe, thrashing about on the table until one's lungs collapsed.

Unsuccessful.

He couldn't watch the other suffer. Shaking, he injected the seizing twin with the lethal dose of phenol. Then she was still, blood pouring from her mouth. Hans washed the blood from his hands—then he threw up. As he dabbed the vomit from his chin, he reminded himself that if he didn't conduct these experiments, somebody else would, and they wouldn't be as merciful.

He heard the click of boots on linoleum and turned. The sight of the SS officer churned Hans' recovering stomach—the sharpness of the uniform, the cold gaze, the threat he posed to Clara. If only Mila knew the toll this job was taking.

"The United Nations troops are surrounding Berlin as we speak," the officer said.

Hans hesitated, cleaning the operating table. "I've heard rumors."

"Aren't you concerned?"

"Excuse me?"

"The Americans will discover what you've been doing here—to children." His voice was condescending.

"Talk like that will get you fired," Hans warned, "or worse."

"The Allies are surrounding the city, Doctor. Berlin will fall and so will Hitler. It's time to face the facts." Oberman's aggressive German accent disappeared, replaced with a crisp, clear American one. "You have one chance to get out alive. We'll help you if you agree to work for us."

"They're offering us protection," Hans whispered that night in bed. Mila's eyes grew wide. "No! The only thing riskier than working for the Führer is working against him. Are you insane?"

"You said it yourself. The Allied powers have won. Hitler's going down, and we're going down with him. I don't see what choice we have."

Mila sighed. "I love you." She placed a hand to Hans' cheek. "And I know you love us, but if anything ever happens to her . . ." She paused. "I will never forgive you."

"This is it." Hans turned off the faucet and maneuvered his hands into latex gloves. He turned toward the cage—his latest experiment. Through his earpiece, Oberman listened, waiting.

Though Hans had operated on chimpanzees before, this one was special. Not only had the polio he'd introduced taken hold, crippling the chimp, but the cure he'd injected was working, too. Chelsea had control over her toes now, but her enclosure made it impossible to tell what more she could do. He took a deep breath and opened the cage. Chelsea scampered out.

"I've done it," Hans shouted. "She can walk!"

He'd found the cure. But Mila's protests echoed in his mind: "Even if it does work, she's a chimp, Hans. Our daughter is not a chimp." So, Hans sent for a girl.

"Here she is, Doctor," his assistant said.

Hans didn't look up from the injection he was preparing until the girl began to cry—the quiet, desperate sound of a child trying to catch her breath between sobs. He'd heard that cry before—in Clara's bedroom the night she'd heard them arguing. He'd held her as she cried. Shaking.

Now, Hans hesitated, picturing his own Little Bell with each tremble of this specimen girl's tiny frame. He injected the virus.

Weeks later, supervised by officers, she began to wiggle her toes, bend her knees. Hans had just received the news when the SS officer entered the operating room and closed the door.

"The Nazis have discovered your daughter," he said.

Hans felt the world crumble beneath his feet. He fell to the ground—loss suffocating him, wrapping its iron fist around his heart. "No."

"Yes, but I've arranged for undercover agents to take her to a safehouse. If you help us, we'll help you. The president needs you."

Hans' heart expanded, hesitantly filling with hope.

The officer reached into his uniform and handed Hans a folded piece of parchment. "Meet me in the tavern in the village of Dresden tonight—just inside the boundaries of American-occupied territory. If you're apprehended, repeat this phrase: the Squire of Hyde Park."

Hans unfolded the paper and read the diagnosis: *President Franklin Delano Roosevelt, poliomyelitis, prognosis grim.*

Hans hurried home. So much was at stake. "Mila!" he called.

The house was silent.

He paused. He heard muffled tears coming from the bedroom. *Scheisse—Clara!*

"Why, God?" Mila cried. "She didn't deserve this!" Mila buried her face in Clara's empty comforter.

"Honey, no. She's okay!" Hans wrapped his arms around her.

Mila flung him away and stood. "How dare you!" she spat—teeth bared, eyes wild, cheeks smeared with streaks of red. "This is your fault, you monster!" She grabbed the copy of *Mein Kampf* from Clara's bedside and hurled it at him. "We could've escaped! Fled! Do you understand? She wouldn't have had to hide. Your little vanity project got in the way. You cared more about your own fame than saving her!"

Speechless, Hans just stared. "Mila. Listen."

She grew quiet, tears streaming down her face. "She's gone. Why don't you care?"

"Because she's safe. The Americans have her."

Mila laughed—a deep, guttural laugh—and left the room. "You're so fucking delusional!" she shouted and reentered, carrying Clara's leg braces, engraved with their daughter's initials. "Josef stopped by today. He found these in the pile of victims' remains. She burned to death, Hans. Fuck the Americans! Fuck your cure!" She tossed the braces at the bed. They clattered to the floor. "I want a divorce," she said and left.

Their daughter was dead. Their marriage was over.

But obstacles did not exist to be surrendered to—only to be broken. Hans had been wrong to trust Oberman. Now, the Americans would pay.

So, Hans ran. Out the door, down the street, adrenaline coursing through his veins. Though he'd run, miles maybe, he wasn't tired.

A small village loomed ahead. Suddenly, the butt of a rifle struck his chest, knocking him to the ground. A fist closed around his throat. "State your business," the man roared and released Hans, cocking his rifle.

Hans coughed, choking back fear. Finally, he managed, "The Squire of Hyde Park."

The man stepped backward, lowering his rifle, his hard expression still alert.

When Hans reached the tavern, he found the undercover officer drinking, casually, as if the world weren't crumbling down around them.

"I need a pint," Hans said, taking a seat at the bar.

"What have you decided?"

"I'll do it."

"Pint's on me, then." Oberman extended his hand. "We leave tonight."

Under the cover of night, Oberman's jeep pulled up in front of Mengele's lab, where Hans collected the vaccine he'd need to carry out the cure. That was just for show. What he was really eager to get his hands on was the phenol.

Supplies in hand, they boarded a cargo plane bound for America. They touched down in Fort Benning—an hour's drive to Warm Springs, Georgia. There, Franklin Delano Roosevelt was waiting for them, receiving his regularly scheduled hydrotherapy—healing.

A young soldier dressed in fatigues leaned against the rehab center, his cap pulled over his eyes, face angled toward the sun. Hans and Oberman approached, startling the man to attention. "IDs," the soldier said.

Oberman produced his card and gestured to Hans. "He's with me."

They were led to a private room with a Secret Service agent in each corner. Eleanor Roosevelt stood at the president's bedside. Hans approached. Spectacles too small for Roosevelt's face rested on his long nose. Wrinkles rippled down his cheeks. The powerful man crippled by polio. Just like Clara.

Eleanor touched Hans' hand. "Thank you for this selfless act. I'm so grateful."

Roosevelt, almost too weak to speak, said, "Yes, thank you, son." A thick, blue vein in his throat rose and fell as he spoke.

"This is for Clara," Hans said, sticking the needle deep into the president's vein.

Roosevelt cringed. The Secret Service agents suspected nothing.

"A deal's a deal, Hans," Oberman said. "Here she is."

Hans turned. "Clara," he whispered and ran to the girl, cradled in the leathery seat of a wheelchair, smiling. "But your braces—I thought you were dead." Hans collapsed at her feet, crying into her lap.

"We disposed of her braces, so the Nazis wouldn't suspect we'd saved her," Oberman said.

Hans wept.

"It's okay, Daddy. I'm here now."

"I'm so sorry, Clara," Hans said.

Behind him, the president gasped, taking one last tortured breath—a slow, steady hum of the monitor—and his heart stopped beating forever.

The Secret Service agents tackled Hans, their weight crushing his lungs. Life as he knew it was over.

Years later, Hans sat, silent, waiting. The courtroom was packed. Lights flashed all around, not an empty seat in the house. A media circus. While the appeal process was usually carried out behind closed doors, the decision to grant a stay of execution to the man who'd killed the president was one the public demanded to partake in. Many people spoke on Hans' behalf or against him. Their stories faded into the background, becoming the soundtrack of his misery as he contemplated all his life had become.

He thought of Clara. Of the little girl he'd infected with polio. The failed Siamese twins. All of the children he'd killed. He thought of their parents who must have loved them as much as he loved his Little Bell. Suddenly, he was crushed by the heft of those children—the thousands of lives lost.

A young girl took the stand, no more than thirteen. She walked unsteadily, a newborn calf unsure of her legs.

"State your name," the judge ordered.

Hans didn't recognize the girl at first. And then she spoke, her voice like bells.

"Clara Shmelzer."

Hans' heart broke.

The judge said, "I understand you want to make a statement on your father's behalf."

"Yes." Clara cleared her throat and delivered her speech. "My father taught me that obstacles are meant to be broken. That's why I'm here. I can't quit on a man who never quit on me. And though you could never replace the lives lost in this ungodly war, you cannot make light of the lives my father has saved." Clara smiled hesitantly at Hans and nodded at the judge.

"Does anyone else have anything to say on this man's behalf?"

There was silence at first. Then, the frantic snapping of cameras, the gasps, the shuffling. One by one, audience members stood, abandoning their wheelchairs forever. Their lives had been saved by the man on trial, and now they did their best to return the favor. Hans looked around wildly. Tears shone in the eyes of many, anger in the eyes of others—a house divided—those who'd lost loved ones and those who'd been saved by the cure. But if there were to be one deciding vote, it would be that of the eight-year-old paralyzed girl he'd once fought so hard for, now a strong, young woman fighting for him. Clara rose, eyes glistening with tears. In this war, men had conspired to play God and failed. But despite everything, humanity survived.

Time would tell if Hans would, too.

Dr. Josef Mengele, a Nazi who conducted horrific human experiments at Auschwitz, 1944.

President Franklin Delano Roosevelt, who had polio but ultimately died from an intracerebral hemorrhage in 1945, pictured here in 1933.

This story is an alternative history that includes real historical figures but mixes fictitious and historical events.

Block 10 at Auschwitz, where Dr. Josef Mengele practiced medical experiments on concentration camp prisoners and supervised the activities of inmate doctors who had been forced to work in the camp's medical service, photographed in 2008.

Child survivors of Auschwitz, wearing adult-sized prisoner uniforms, with several of the children being sets of twins—one of Mengele's experimental fascinations in his anthropological and heredity studies—during the camp's liberation by Soviets in 1945.

The Train

Anique Sara Taylor

France 1943.

W e huddle, freeze-framed
stems into embankments next
to railroad tracks that promise life.

Aligned with the iron churn
and clank of a German ammunition
train, we sprint beside it, leap to boxcar

rungs, clutch side ladder, clamber
to the top where we regroup. SS soldiers
travel in tandem below us in posh troop cars.

My shoe slips
off the metal crossbar.

One   step.
One.   Missed.   Rung.

I flutter from the thread
of my wrist. Feet thrash, almost
slam against the frozen planet that spins
inches away from my tiny bones. Afraid roots
hungry for blood will try to pull me back into the earth.

They gather on boxcar
roof as the cars accelerate. Is
someone missing? I cling, alive still in
this hollow second, before I splinter into the void.

His shadow silhouetted against indigo sky
hurtles train top to train top, searching for me.
He hollers down. The first body, an anchor, fastens
himself to boxcar roof, grabs onto the next. The third locks
legs. His opening spine unfolds upside down, lowering torso.
Arms stretch a human link that reaches for the disappearing thread
of me, that hugs the speeding train's side wall, yellow heat of velocity—

until his clutch of stone.
Sinews of his hands wrestle
my ghost back into a wish for life.

A train from Bergen-Belsen filled with Holocaust prisoners
is liberated by the United States Army near Madgeburg /
Farsleben, Prussian Saxony, Germany, 1945.

This poem is based on a true story from Yad Vashem, found in The Righteous among the Nations: Rescuers of Jews during the Holocaust, *by Mordecai Paldiel. More Holocaust survivor and rescuer testimonials can be found at yadvashem.org.*

A cattle car used to deport Slovak Jews—SŽ stands for *Slovenské Železnice* (Slovak Railways)—to the Sereď concentration camp in Slovakia, photographed in 2017.

The openings on cattle wagons like this one—now preserved at Fort van Breendonk, Belgium, photographed in 2007— were covered in barbed wire when the cars were used for the transport of Belgian Jews to camps in Eastern Europe.

Secrets

P. D. R. Lindsay

She spread her toes, pressing them firmly into the sun-baked dust so that it rose above the joints. Just for one blink it felt cool, then it was hot and itchy again. *Why do I have to do this? I hate them, hate them all.*

Carefully she chose another patch, stepped into it, and squished her toes. More coolth. She kept moving sideways, just another foot's span, squirming her toes this time, watching the little puffs of dust, sniffing at the burned-stone smell.

Her lower lip curled. *Sister won't let me be with the big girls, but I'm not in kindergarten.* She nipped her lips together as she remembered her mother jerking her away from the little girls and boys lined up the day before, clamoring, the kids eager to go with the soldiers. She'd wanted to go, too.

"Not with them," her mother had cried, yanking her wrist so hard it hurt. But she wouldn't say why, and the kindergarten children had all gone, along with most of her classmates, marched off to the trucks, with many of the Sisters, to be driven down from the plateau to the steamy heat of the jungle below.

Everything was wrong. The looks, the bitten-off words, the weight of unsaid things pressing around them all, pushing against her chest, squeezing her heart, shortening her breath. The way her mother didn't look at the soldiers.

"Don't frighten the children, for God's sake," she'd heard her mother say to them. That's what all the mothers said. And no one would tell her anything, least of all where her father and brothers had gone. She wanted her daddy—he knew she could keep secrets.

There. She could see the edge of the veranda. Head down, seeming to stare at her toes and the gritty dust clouds they made, she sneaked a quick glance under the shadow of her falling hair. The soldiers' part of the veranda was empty.

"Just look carefully, Brigit—see if the Japanese soldiers are there," her mother said, "then come back to Sister Beatrice. Make it look like you're playing."

Carefully she made a toe-squirming turn, pressing and squishing her feet twice more. She sneezed the dust out of her nose. Then, hair flapping as she jumped around, she dipped out of sight behind the school building.

"Well?" The big girls pounced. They grabbed at her, and she squeaked, rubbing at their tight hands.

"Gently, Rosa, Catherine." Sister Beatrice smiled and touched their arms.

The girls eased their grips and fidgeted.

"What did you see, Brigit?" Sister Beatrice asked.

Brigit shuffled her feet, uneasy under their intense eyes. *What was it? What was their secret?* She ducked the demanding stares, half turned, and let her gaze drift, looking between the buildings, across the plateau, to the two volcano peaks, one on either side of the school. Clear and sharp against the heavy blue sky, Sinabung and Sibajak weren't smoking today. Even the jungle below them was still. No monkey screams, no whooping and trilling from the birds.

"Brigit?"

She was aware of impatience, even from Sister. And Sister wouldn't tell. Brigit asked her what was happening. *What would the soldiers do?* But Sister wouldn't say. No adult would. Yet they whispered endlessly. Why did they want her to spy on the soldiers? *I'm not stupid. I can keep a secret, but what is it?*

"They aren't out yet," Brigit finally said.

"Good girl. Come along with me." Sister took her hand, pulling her as if she were a baby.

Brigit jerked free. She was nearly eight, not five.

Sister caught her elbow, gently squeezing it. "It's all right," Sister said.

But it wasn't, was it? Sister's voice said it wasn't.

At the far end of the school, Sister made Brigit join the few remaining kindergarten girls, children like she, who had their mothers and older sisters here with them.

"Sister!"

"Hush now, Brigit. There's a good girl."

But I'm not in kindergarten. Even Mummy wouldn't let me be one of them. Brigit wound her dark hair behind her ears and tried to understand. *I should be moving up into the real dormitory.* She wriggled, anticipating the pleasure. The dormitory had always been her goal. She couldn't understand why the big girls, the twelve-year-olds, always insisted on single rooms again. *I won't, and when I'm thirteen and move off to higher school, I'll ask to sleep in a dormitory, too.*

Sister caught her hand and led her forward. "Help us now. You can do it, Brigit. Show your friends how to run and chase. Ready, steady, go."

How she loved this running barefoot through the dust. It was like before the Japanese soldiers came. *No, forget, just run.*

Three of the big girls were in the lead. Sister lumbered close behind her. Rosa chased the little ones. They ran right past the soldiers' end of the school, squealing, forming a long chain as each one was tagged. Then round they went, dancing in circles, all the time Sister Beatrice and the big girls watching with sideways looks, wary of that veranda.

Where had her sister gone? Letty disappeared here every time. *Why?* Letty and Rosa did this every time they played the chasing games. Brigit squirmed around, looking for them.

"Don't look. Hold my hand, Brigit. There. No, don't let the soldiers know we're watching." Sister pulled gently, smiling, coaxing.

Brigit gave in. Pressed into the circle, she went around and around again. She hated this, so near them, and the big girls singing that song. Softly the words came:

"Ching Chong Chinamen,
You Japanese smell.
Jesus sees what you do,
And you'll go to hell."

Brigit hesitated, her skin creeping. They would come. She watched Sister's face in wonder as Sister sang the rhyme. Sister even sang that word, the hell word. Her smile was wide and warm, but she said hell, and her eyes were firmly not looking at the side of the house where the vegetable gardens were, full of all that food the big girls planted and the soldiers took.

Was that the secret? Did Letty still raid the garden like the big girls used to before the Japanese came? Or was it the bins behind their building where such wonderful food was dumped uneaten? Brigit was always hungry now. They all were.

"Look at me, Brigit. Sing with us," Sister ordered.

Brigit didn't want to sing that song in English. Some of the officers spoke English—she'd heard them. *I want to sing in Indonesian. The officermen don't speak it.*

Catherine broke free and led the kindergarten girls, weaving the little ones in and out of the circle. Above the squeals and giggles, the pat-padding of bare feet in the thick dust, Brigit heard hard boot soles clop on the wooden veranda floor.

Them!

Brigit tugged at Sister Beatrice's hand.

"Yes, I see, Brigit. Come now, little ones, make a circle again."

Brigit squinted sideways through her fringe. It was the young officermen. They only watched. The big girls sang louder and pulled the little ones about. Brigit was pushed through the group, and all the girls cried out.

"After her!" Sister called, and feet stamped in the dust.

Brigit dodged and darted. She had to stay in the open until Sister called her. If Brigit didn't, the big girls pinched her, and her mother scolded. *Why? It wasn't fair. No one said. And Mummy is always cross with me now.*

She looped around in front of the veranda and dashed for the far fence. She knew just where the guards would yell and wave their guns. She ran screaming at them. The little ones screamed behind her.

"Go back," the guards yelled in Indonesian.

She stuck out her tongue. "Squinty-eyed, yellow toads," she screeched at them in glee and jumped around, running straight through the little girls, pulling them roughly around, dragging them back with her. They straggled across the dusty patch that once had been the school lawn, and Sister Beatrice spread her arms to gather them in. They were called back.

"A good run, Brigit. You did that well." Sister patted her cheek.

Brigit felt her mouth curl into a smile. Sister was nice. She leaned into Sister's solid thigh, hoping for a hug.

"Best find your mother now," Sister said, ruffling her hair.

She won't want me. She'll be fussing with Letty, hugging her, keeping her near. Brigit hadn't had a proper hug since the Japanese arrived. The older girls got them all. *Why? What did I do wrong?*

Her mother merely ran a light, distracted hand over Brigit's hair—Mother's tight, pinched eyes looking beyond her to Letty. "Run away and play. Go to Nona's room."

Brigit opened her mouth to speak.

"Please don't make a fuss. There's an important meeting this morning. Keep away. Help me by playing with the other little children. Only stay out of the way, down at Nona's, you understand?"

Brigit swallowed around a hard place in her throat and looked at her mother, then at Letty. *It isn't fair. All I do is play with the babies, and even you say I'm too old to play with them. No, I don't understand. Tell me. What's the secret?* But she didn't know how to say the words to a mother who didn't listen or even see her. Brigit stomped off, sucking the uncombed ends of her hair. It was growing, but she didn't want plaits again. She'd have to persuade Nona to cut it. *I'll go catch her a snake, and then maybe she'll cut my hair.*

Nona's rooms, the last three of the long stretch of school buildings that faced the lawn, were far away from the soldiers. Nona liked Brigit—they shared a secret, the secret of the snakes. No one else knew. The soldiers took the fruit, the vegetables, all the stores, gave out only a handful of rice per person. Snakes were plentiful and tasted like chicken the way Nona cooked them. So, Brigit and Nona hunted snakes. The best snakes for eating, those dark, thick ratcatchers, hidden in the boxed-in space under the building. Brigit ducked under Nona's back steps, picked the flour sack from between the beams, and wriggled down below the building into the darkness.

Wait in the dark until I can see. Watch my feet for snakes.

The space under Nona's rooms was almost empty, only two tin trunks left. Brigit paused, half bent to avoid the wooden floor above her, wrinkling her nose to catch the snake smell over the damp earth. Nona had taught her about snakes.

Smell them. Listen for their skin on the ground.

Brigit stepped slowly, watchful. The slits of sunshine through the veranda-side wall made her blink. She dropped onto her hands and knees, crawled toward the light, and began her hunt, crouching, creeping slowly across the packed earth.

A movement ahead, a slur across the dirt. *Snake.* Brigit padded softly, slowly toward it, toward the soldiers' end of the school. She smiled. She liked it under here, hidden in the dark. The snake raised its head and swerved toward the gaps in the veranda planks. Brigit knew it was hers. It was coming right to her. She reached forward, ready to pounce.

Above her head, the planks jounced and rattled. The snake flicked around. Brigit grabbed it by the tail and whipped it through the space, cracking it twice like a silent whip thong, then thumped it against the wooden uprights. She wrapped it in Nona's flour bag, then listened to the boots marching down the veranda. She could not see up, no cracks to spy through, but the feet thundered over her head, making the wooden boards dip and sway. Brigit covered her ears and crouched until the feet tromped away. She listened. Somewhere something moved. Veranda boards creaked. The high-pitched roar of an angry voice, Him, the chief of soldiers, reached her. Boots crashed, de dum, and stilled. Guns slap-flapped, thumped to the floor. Brigit shook the noise from her head, concentrated again, and saw the second snake. It glided along the veranda space, hurrying to escape the commotion above. She scurried forward, rushing eagerly, but the snake flowed sideways in a zigzag of swiftness and squeezed through the planks into the bright sunlit world outside.

Oh, vomit, vomit, vomit. It was the rudest word she knew she could say.

"Bring her to me."

Brigit startled violently and bit her tongue. That voice. His. Above her head. He spoke English. Brigit melted into the dry soil and sucked at the hurt.

"You say you don't know where the records are, Sister?"

"I am a teaching Sister, not an administrator."

That was Sister Beatrice. Brigit lifted her head. This must be the meeting her mother meant. She hadn't said it was with the soldiers.

"And you don't know where the records are, or if they are destroyed or who destroyed them?" His voice dropped.

Brigit strained to hear, then flinched as he thundered out Japanese commands. The veranda floorboards jolted. And again. Boots and rifle butts clattered on hard wood and thwacked on something softer.

A wail. Voices—one she was sure was her mother's—protests, words clashing. More slammed boots, more rifle butts. Screams. Voices. Then silence. And his voice, raised, speaking Japanese, then English. Brigit bolted, heading for Nona's.

But Nona had the little children lined up outside. Three of the soldiers stood guard. Brigit stopped. Her stomach clenched and hurt again. Guns swung toward her. She felt her scalp rise.

"Go and fetch the mothers, Brigit. Find these little ones' mothers." The guns moved to point at Nona until she said it all again in Indonesian. Then the guns raised, slapped back against shoulders.

The pain went, breath came back. Brigit stomped down the veranda beside a young soldier, wrinkling her nose in disgust.

"Ching Chong Chinaman," she sang softly, knowing he could not understand. *And they did smell funny.*

Suddenly the soldier grabbed her elbow, wrenched her straight, and there he was, the chief officer. Blocking the veranda. Staring at her.

A gabble of high-pitched talk began. Brigit waited, rolling from one bare foot to the other. She felt the flour bag string slip a little. Tugging at her dress, she tried to hook the string around her sash. A sleeve blurred her vision. Her bag was ripped away from her and emptied. The snake rolled flaccidly up to the officer's shiny bootcaps. Brigit tried to scoop up the snake and was jerked away, half lifted by her sash.

"So, a snake. To frighten us with?" He shook her before dropping her onto the planking. The soldier poked at the snake, trying to push it off the veranda.

"That's mine," Brigit grabbed it and wrapped it into her dress hem. She glared up into the strange faces. *Mustn't tell.* "I killed it."

The officer's black eyes burned hers. She backed away through the open French windows behind her. His hand gripped her shoulders, turned her, and thrust her onto the veranda.

"Do the children know, Sister?"

Know what?

Sister Beatrice was sitting in the nearest chair, two soldiers crowding her, their rifle butts on the ground, barrels leaning in toward her. Her face was paper white. Brigit couldn't see her mother in the crush. The soldiers made a brown fence between the pale faces. And the big girls were all there, cornered, knotted into a tight group, white as Sister Beatrice. The grip on Brigit's shoulder squeezed fiercely. She squirmed, trying to wriggle free.

"Does this child know how old the girls are?" His voice. His hand. His rage.

Brigit sagged under the weight of it all.

Sister Beatrice spoke. Her voice quavered. "She's just a little girl."

Sister Beatrice!

A murmur of agreement from the mothers.

"I am not. I'm nearly eight!" But she spoke in Indonesian to be safe.

Her escorting soldier knelt on one knee beside her. *His skin is yellow, but his eyes are all brown, not like black-eyed Him.* She looked, a rapid sideways glance, at that dangerous face. The officer stared across the room at the big girls, but his grip on her shoulder never lightened.

"Only eight. You're a quick one," the soldier replied. He spoke in Indonesian, too. "Clever! Did you catch the snake? How did you do that?"

Brigit trembled under his words, trying to keep Nona's secret and not say something that would give it away. *What was safe to say?*

"Could your sister catch one? That's your sister, isn't she?" He pointed to Rosa.

"No, that's Rosa. Letty's my sister." She pointed with her chin.

"Oh, the fair one. She couldn't catch a snake, could she?"

Brigit shook her head. "The big girls don't."

"She's too big? Thirteen, is she?"

"No, our school isn't a higher school. Only up to twelve, then we . . ."

44

Something stirred, a sound among the mothers who spoke in Indonesian. Movements began around the room, were suppressed as the soldiers raised their rifles.

Her soldier spoke to Him.

He turned to look at Brigit, then spoke to Sister Beatrice. "So . . . these oldest girls, in the highest class, they are twelve, then."

Silence. A silence that made Brigit's skin crawl.

"Take them," he said in English and threw Brigit at Sister's feet.

There was a dreadful noise from mothers and big girls. A rising, wailing "No." The soldiers moved, shoving, smacking mothers away, barring the big girls in.

"Shave their heads, escort them to the main camp. They can earn their food as comfort girls for the soldiers."

Brigit lifted her head. *What was happening? What were comfort girls?* The first thing she saw were Sister's socks. They were dirty. Sister Beatrice's socks were dirty, sticky red patching the white. Then she saw her mother's face, all crumpled, with two slow tears crawling down. Mother wouldn't look at Brigit.

What's wrong? What did I say? Was that the secret? Why didn't they say?

"Mummy," Brigit whispered, then fell silent.

Indonesian *Jugan lanfu* ("comfort women") at a Japanese *ianjo* ("comfort station") during the Asian Pacific War, between 1931 and 1945.

Korean comfort girls rescued in Burma, being questioned by officers of the G-2 Myitkyina Task Force of the U.S. Army, on August 14, 1944.

Chinese and Malayan comfort girls forcibly taken from Penang by the Japanese to work as comfort girls, shown here during the allied reoccupation of the Andaman Islands, c. 1945.

The Birthday Party, 1944

Clare Chu

I didn't want to go to the party. I didn't know the birthday girl. It was across the river. Sandor, my brother, came. Sandor—dashing, wild, my escort. He played the piano for the birthday girl. She blushed. I examined the newly minted stain on her pink frock. The notes faded. I felt the soft rumble of faraway planes. The fluttering wings of moths. We held our breath, then blew out ten candles. German soldiers blew up our bridges. Balls of fire sizzling in the water. Insistent, loud, furious. Dividing Budapest into Buda and Pest. We couldn't go home until the river froze. Until we could walk on the ice.

Germans within, Soviets without. The noose ever tightening. The servants gone. Mamma couldn't pay them, couldn't feed them. Only Marta stayed. Her whiskers tickling my neck, she kissed me goodnight. She had forgotten where she came from. She had no place to go. My parents' precious horse, Nimrod, was put out to pasture. No racing, no flying past the cheering crowds. No thrills for him in the winner's enclosure. Eaten later by a Soviet general loath to dine on his own horse. Mamma was in denial. The Red Army overran the city. Marta hid Sandor and me in the cellar. Fists in our mouths. Dismal, dark, but safe.

Stomping in the house. Shouts on the stairs. Fat, bald, the stench. *What have we here?* Hands grabbing. *Look at you.* Fear. *Yuri, leave her, too young, no breasts.* Sandor cries, *I'll give you my watch. Patek Philippe, my father's.* Defender of mankind. *We'll take them both.* Hands on me. Grimy fingernails. Voracious fingers inside me.

I look out through the broken window. A fly is trapped in the dust, one leg shaking. Mothers scream from the shell-shocked tombs. Over the bloated cemetery, the sinking fog is blind.

Army without a Country

Johannah Racz Knudson

The Czechoslovak Legion in Siberia, 1914-1920.

I ride a recognized route   (a negotiation at every stop).   I used to be in Spain   (a recognized state).   Our troops take Vladivostok in the name of a country that does not exist. Spain was full of decoration   (loose beads, ribbons, uniforms, languages). I think of her waking, words I almost understand   (condensation on glass).   She asked many different ways. She explained. She said it with different words, three different languages. (Romanian is like Italian. Italian is similar to Spanish.)   I speak Czech and Ukrainian and German and Russian and Romanian, all native tongues. I understand after two thousand miles of track (ten rifles for every hundred men).   At Kursk, the soviet demands 216 machine guns and 21,000 rifles. Jan hides grenades in the grain bin. We won't give any more after Chelyabinsk. We cover ourselves with rugs, belt them around our waists in winter months.   (I think of words and hold a gun, one for every hundred men.)   (She tried every language.)   The train keeps moving. They take our weapons. They take my shoes. I have no uniform. My country is an idea. Grenades are apples. Grenades are eggs. We eat. We see red. Jan loses a leg. I see snow and flags and blood. Men die. Some live. Her tongue remains. A country begins.

The Girl from No Gun Ri

Esther Ra

> *During the Korean War, on July 26-29, 1950,*
> *between 250 and 400 South Korean refugees*
> *were killed in a U.S. air attack and fire from the*
> *7th Cavalry Regiment at a bridge near the vil-*
> *lage of No Gun Ri. The U.S. military, fearing*
> *North Korean infiltrators in disguise, ordered*
> *soldiers to shoot South Korean refugee groups.*

I.

I was sixteen when they came
war had broken out   and girls
were the price of cigarettes
older women swung scythes
like broken teeth at soldiers
who were said to ----   the girls
so I hid in an urn in the dark
waiting for history to pass
my name was Park Hee-Sook
I wore my hair long   in a braid
tipped with a rippling ribbon
smooth as the flow of red blood

II.

my playground became a battleground
and we gathered our skirts to flee
home became a fistful of objects
pounding its dirge on my back
the communists are coming   they said
you must move out or die they said
in the sun   everything   was too hot
I can't breathe   the Americans
said *keep walking* I cannot

III.

then the sky split and the universe
was a crematory

                    flaring

everything   was in pieces
                              mother
father   sister   home
                 body   leg   arm   head
   earthclod   cattle   burning
where   am I
      human meat   we are all

on fire

IV.

        orphaned in a day, I wear
the torn bodies of the dead,

        hiding from a horde
of black bullets

       I hear blood gurgle and burst
in the strafed tunnels,

       a cacophony of flies
feed on swollen flesh

       my throat burns like paper
in the dark, I don't know

       if I'm drinking
water or blood

       if I stay I will die
if I leave   I will die

       if I die   I will die
I run out

V.

an American waves me forward
and men clamber out of their holes

I say *Hello Hello*
the only English word I know

Hello my whole family
has been killed

it is hell in there *Hello*
I cry coated in blood

I scream *Hello Hello*
and pound on their chests

51

you said you would save us
Hello

I am red ribboned with
the dark hands of death

as they hold me shaking
in their arms

Hello I cry
to the living and dead

as I weep all the bones
from my body

VI.

      In the village, the nights
have burning blue eyes

      I cannot stop my own eyes
from drowning.

      The watchmen remember
my racking with wails

      as ghosts clog my throat
with their names.

      Before the war ends
I walk back to the bridge

      and search for remains
of my father

I scoop up his flesh
in the cup of my hands

and bury him
far from his home

O my father rest here
in the dark of the earth

as I braid your spirit
from the past

O my father hide here
in the mouth of the land

Hundreds of thousands
of Koreans fled south
after the North Korean
army struck across the
border, c. mid-1950.

as we wait
for history   to pass

"The Girl from No Gun Ri" draws from testimonies and descriptions of Park Hee-Sook, a survivor of the No Gun Ri incident, as described in The Bridge at No Gun Ri: A Hidden Nightmare from the Korean War. *Charles J. Hanley, Sang-hun Choe, and Martha Mendoza, with researcher Randy Herschaft. Henry Holt and Company, New York, 2001.*

53

An excerpt from U.S. Ambassador (to South Korea) John J. Muccio's memo informing Assistant Secretary of State Dean Rusk that the U.S. Army has decided to fire on South Korean refugees approaching U.S. lines. The letter is dated July 26, 1950, the day the U.S. 7th Cavalry Regiment began shooting refugees at No Gun Ri.

Text from above memo excerpt (all sic):

Yesterday evening a meeting was arranged, by 8th Army HQ request, at the office of the Home Minister at the temporary Capitol. G-1, G-2, Provost Marshall, CIC, the Embassy, the Home and Social Affairs Ministries, and the Director of National Police. The following decisions were made:

1. Leaflet drops will be made north of US lines warning the people not to proceed south, that they risk being fired upon if they do so. If refugees do appear from north of US lines they will receive warning shots, and if they then persist in advancing they will be shot.

The circles show bullet holes left in one side of the No Gun Ri bridge from the U.S. military massacre against Korean refugees that took place at this location in July 1950, photographed here in October 2015.

The twin-underpass railroad bridge at No Gun Ri, South Korea, where U.S. military killed a large number of South Korean refuges in 1950, photographed here in 1960.

II. FACTS BEARING ON THE PROBLEM:

2. It is reported that large groups of civilians, either composed of or controlled by North Korean soldiers, are infiltrating U. S. positions.

3. The army has requested that we strafe all civilian refugee parties that are noted approaching our positions.

4. To date, we have complied with the army request in this respect.

An excerpt from a July 25, 1950, memo of Colonel Turner C. Rogers, the operations chief for the U.S. Air Force in South Korea, that states U.S. warplanes are strafing refugees at the U.S. Army's request, for fear that the refugees are KPA forces in disguise.

Text from above memo excerpt (all sic):
II. <u>FACTS BEARING ON THE PROBLEM:</u>

2. It is reported that large groups of civilians, either composed of or controlled by North Korean soldiers, are infiltrating U. S. positions.

3. The army has requested that we strafe all civilian refugee parties that are noted approaching our positions.

4. To date, we have complied with the army request in this respect.

The Death of History

Jahman Hill

*For Henry Smith, Delano Middleton, Samuel Hammond, Jr.,
and all Black men and women murdered by the state
but left out of history books. We will not forget.*

The following story has been on repeat:

I turned on the news today
And saw they killed another
Black Boy
His Name was History
Apparently, the officer saw him wielding justice and thought
That if History got out, he could be of some danger to
the police and the rest of America

History was wearing a coat the color February
His jacket said "Orangeburg,"
The size was a mere 1968,
But to the officer it looked more like a size 2016
History may have just been a boy, but to the officer
History was menacing,
Had the strength of three Black teens
And ran like college students fleeing from buckshot
on their own campus

When the officer was confronted with History
He immediately fired his fear
Didn't even give History a chance to explain himself
I guess History was so dangerous the officer didn't
want to take him in for booking
Had no choice but to pull out his fear and unload
multiple rounds of ignorance, hatred, and racism
into History's back

When asked about the incident
Officer White said
He used his fear instead of the non-lethal rationality
because an irrational reaction is so commonplace
among cops they now label it objectively reasonable
They covered History's body with law
Blanketed his appendages with amendments
The chalk outline looked like denial
But it was made of mendacity
South Carolina's state officials mourned the death of History
Sad because History tarnished the state's reputation
They'd always known History was trouble
But as long as they could keep him quiet
Nobody would know he was there
The news said that History was left there dying for hours
His blood seeped into the concrete
Left a stain that would be scrubbed out but never fully gone
The asphalt would bubble under summer suns
Producing a foul odor like chitlins at the old Baptist church
It was forced upon us like an unwanted religion
Every time we spoke in tongues and danced the dance
of our native Gods
Sister Smith would get a fan and a bottle of water
When Mama fell out, they would cover her with a cloth
the same way they covered up History
Whose blood ran through Mama's bones

You know,
They say if you listen close enough
You can still hear History whispering in the night
Begging for someone to listen to his story
You know the pictures they show of History
don't even look like him
The police changed his whole face
Covered his body with law
Blanketed his appendages with amendments
They shot down History in a size 1968
But by the time they got to his body
He had grown to 2016

The Orangeburg massacre began as a protest against racial segregation at the All-Star Bowling Lane in Orangeburg, South Carolina, when Black students from South Carolina State University were told to leave the building, resulting in 200 protestors returning later to occupy the parking lot of the bowling alley, on February 5, 1968. When the protestors returned, police were waiting for them with billy clubs, and 8 protestors were sent to the hospital. The bowling alley closed in 2007, but the building remains and is on the National Register of Historic Places for its vital role in the massacre. Photographed here in April 2015.

On the night of February 8, 1968, student demonstrators started a bonfire on the front lawn of the South Carolina State University, a historically Black university, protesting the segregation at the bowling alley and the treatment of fellow Black students who'd been beaten and arrested. As tensions escalated, the South Carolina Highway Patrol fired into the group of protestors, killing two protestors and one passerby, and injuring at least 28 others, most of whom were shot in the back while fleeing. Photo licensed by Getty Images.

Delano Middleton, 17, was a high-school student who was not involved with the protest but was walking to the campus, where his mother worked, when he was killed by police in the Orangeburg massacre, 1968.

Samuel Hammond, Jr., 18 (middle), and Henry Smith, 19 (right), were both South Carolina State University students killed by police in the Orangeburg massacre, 1968.

Mississippi Buried

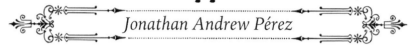

Jonathan Andrew Pérez

A bear lies dormant
   creased with Mississippi wood, a white-throated sparrow
sweltered in alleys and nooks dripped
from hot Meridian woods.

Andrew Goodman, Michael Schwerner, and James Chaney
from Meridian, Mississippi, stopped at a light;
no, smothered, raked with the Ole Miss
downed the Magnolia Trees,
a freedom-guided crew to educate beyond literacy
a school to guarantee that the dam won't break.
She roars
dark rivers and leaves pour
down

reservoirs of white, torched the congregation,
shook the limbs of justice,
awoke a large bear.

Neshoba County sheriff and the white knights
left behind bodies in the dark thorns,
bulldozed county soil.

The first man who talks is dead, dead, dead!

The leaping flames
across the unsaid night,
I close my eyes
and think of water.

They are memorialized by the ashes of the moon,
graced by her presence.

MISSING CALL FBI

THE FBI IS SEEKING INFORMATION CONCERNING THE DISAPPEARANCE AT PHILADELPHIA, MISSISSIPPI, OF THESE THREE INDIVIDUALS ON JUNE 21, 1964. EXTENSIVE INVESTIGATION IS BEING CONDUCTED TO LOCATE GOODMAN, CHANEY, AND SCHWERNER, WHO ARE DESCRIBED AS FOLLOWS:

ANDREW GOODMAN   **JAMES EARL CHANEY**   **MICHAEL HENRY SCHWERNER**

RACE:	White	Negro	White
SEX:	Male	Male	Male
DOB:	November 23, 1943	May 30, 1943	November 6, 1939
POB:	New York City	Meridian, Mississippi	New York City
AGE:	20 years	21 years	24 years
HEIGHT:	5'10"	5'7"	5'9" to 5'10"
WEIGHT:	150 pounds	135 to 140 pounds	170 to 180 pounds
HAIR:	Dark brown; wavy	Black	Brown
EYES:	Brown	Brown	Light blue
TEETH:		Good: none missing	
SCARS AND MARKS:		1 inch cut scar 2 inches above left ear.	Pock mark center of forehead, slight scar on bridge of nose, appendectomy scar, broken leg scar.

SHOULD YOU HAVE OR IN THE FUTURE RECEIVE ANY INFORMATION CONCERNING THE WHEREABOUTS OF THESE INDIVIDUALS, YOU ARE REQUESTED TO NOTIFY ME OR THE NEAREST OFFICE OF THE FBI. TELEPHONE NUMBER IS LISTED BELOW.

DIRECTOR
FEDERAL BUREAU OF INVESTIGATION
UNITED STATES DEPARTMENT OF JUSTICE
WASHINGTON, D. C. 20535
TELEPHONE, NATIONAL 8-7117

June 29, 1964

An FBI missing-persons flier dated June 29, 1964, featuring the faces of murdered civil rights activists (left to right) Andrew Goodman, James Chaney, and Michael Schwerner.

The located remains of Chaney, Goodman, and Schwerner at a premeditated dam site at Olen Burrage's 253-acre Old Jolly Farm, in Philadelphia, Mississippi, on August 4, 1964, a month and a half after the victims had gone missing. Burrage had bragged at an earlier Ku Klux Klan meeting about his dam being a good place to bury the civil rights workers, days before the young men were killed and buried in a hollow at the dam site by a Caterpillar D-4 bulldozer. FBI Director J. Edgar Hoover, frustrated with not being able to locate the bodies, turned to the Colombo mob crime family to crack the case, and a mobster was able to gain the location from a Klansman held at gunpoint. Burrage, who had waited at his farm at midnight to direct the Klansmen to the dam site and had gone to his trucking company's garage to get gasoline to burn the victims' car, was acquitted in the 1967 "Mississippi Burning" trial.

A historical marker for the murders sits at the location of the burned Mt. Zion Church, one of 37 Black churches that were firebombed by Klansmen in Mississippi during the "Freedom Summer" of 1964. Chaney, Goodman, and Schwerner were murdered when they investigated the church burning. This marker was photographed in June 2012.

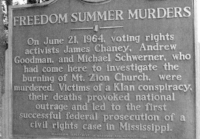

FREEDOM SUMMER MURDERS

On June 21, 1964, voting rights activists James Chaney, Andrew Goodman, and Michael Schwerner, who had come here to investigate the burning of Mt. Zion Church, were murdered. Victims of a Klan conspiracy, their deaths provoked national outrage and led to the first successful federal prosecution of a civil rights case in Mississippi.

A Confession of Conspiracy

Horace Doyle Barnette

*Signed statement written on November 20, 1964,
Horace Doyle Barnette's confession to the FBI about his (convicted)
involvement in the "Mississippi Burning" murders (all sic).*

"I, Horace Doyle Barnette, do hereby make this free and voluntary statement to Special Agent Henry Rask and Special Agent James A. Wooten, who have identified themselves to me to be special agents of the Federal Bureau of Investigation[,] and Special Agent Henry Rask ha[s] informed me that I do not have to make a statement, that any statement made by me can be used against me in a court of law[,] and that I am entitled to consult with an attorney before making this statement and that if I can not afford an attorney and I am required to appear in court, the court will appoint one for me. That no force, threats or promises were made to induce me to make this statement. I presently reside at Cullen, La [Louisiana]. I am 26 years old and was born on September 11, 1938, at Plain Dealing, La.

"On June 21, 1964[,] about 8:00 [p.m.], I was having supper at Jimmy Arledge's house, Meridian, Mississippi. Travis Barnette called Arledge on the telephone and told Arledge that the Klan had a job and wanted to know if Arledge and I could go. Arledge asked me if I could go[,] and we went to [Bernard L.] Akin[']s trailer park on Highway 80 in Meridian, Miss. We did not know what the job was.

"Upon arriving at Akin[']s trailer park we were met by Preacher [Edgar Ray] Killen, Mr. Akins [NB: Akin, not Akins], Jim Jordan and [Alton] Wayne [Roberts]. I do not know Wayne's last name, but I do know his brother is a police officer in Meridian, Miss. Killen told

Killen	Wayne

us that three civil rights workers were in jail in Philadelphia, Miss., and that these three civil rights workers were going to be released from jail and that we were going to catch them and give them a whipping. We were given brown cloth gloves and my car was filled with gas from Mr. Akin[']s gas tank. Jim Snowden, who works for Troy Laundry in Meridian[,] came to Akin[']s trailer park, too. Arledge, Snowden, and Jordan got into my car[,] and we drove to Philadelphia [Mississippi]. Killen and Wayne left before we did[,] and we were told that we would meet him there. Killen had a 1962 or 1961 white Buick. When we arrived in Philadelphia, about 9:30 [p.m.], we met Killen and he got into my car and directed me where to park and wait for someone to tell us when the three civil rights workers were being released from jail. While we were talking, Killen stated that 'we have a place to bury them, and a man to run the dozer to cover them up.' This was the first time I realized that the three civil rights workers were to be killed. About 5 or 10 minutes after we parked, a patrolman from Philadelphia came to the car and said that 'they [the civil rights workers] are going toward Meridian on Highway 19.' We proceeded out Highway 19 and caught up to a Mississippi State Patrol [c]ar, who pulled into a store on the left[-]hand side of the road. We pulled along side of the patrol car[,] and then another car from Philadelphia pulled in between us. I was driving a 1957 Ford, 4 door, 2 tone blue bearing Louisiana license. The Philadelphia car was a 1958 Chevrolet, 2 door and color maroon. It also had a dent on front right[-]hand fender next to the light. No one got out of the cars, but the driver of the Philadelphia car, who I later learned was named [Billy] Posey, talked to the patrolmen. Posey then drove away and we followed. About 2 or 3 miles down the [h]ighway[,] Posey's car stopped and pulled off on the right[-]hand side of the road. Posey motioned for me to go ahead. I then drove fast and caught up to the car that the three civil rights workers were in, pulled over to

the side of the road and stopped. About a minute or 2 later, Deputy Sheriff [Cecil] Price came along and stopped on the pavement beside my car. Jordan asked him who was going to stop them and Price said that he would and took after them and we followed. The

Price

[c]ivil [r]ights workers turned off Highway 19 on to a side road and drove about a couple of miles before Price stopped them. Price stopped his car behind the 1963 Ford Fairlane Station Wagon driven by the [c]ivil [r]ights [w]orkers and we stopped behind Price's car. Price was driving a 1956 Chevrolet, 2 door and 2 tone blue in color. Price stated [to the civil rights workers,] 'I thought you were going back to Meridian if we let you out of jail.' The [c]ivil [r]ights [w]orkers stated that they were[,] and Price asked them why they were taking the long way around. Price told them to get out and get into his car. They got out of their car and proceed[ed] to get into Price's car[,] and then Price took his blackjack and struck [James] Chaney on the back of the head.

"At the junction of Highway 19 and where we turned off, I had let Arledge out of the car to signal the fellows in the Philadelphia car. We then turned around and proceeded back toward Philadelphia. The first car to start back was Price and he had Jim Jordan in the front seat with him and the three civil rights workers in the back seat. I followed next and picked up Arledge at the junction of Highway 19. Snowden drove the 1963 Ford, belonging to the [c]ivil [r]ights [w]orkers. When we came to Posey's car[,] Price and Snowden pulled over to the left side of the [h]ighway and stopped in front of Posey's car. I stopped behind it. Wayne and Posey and the other men from Philadelphia got into the 1963 Ford and rode with Snowden. I do not know how many men were from Philadelphia. Price then started first and I pulled in behind him[,] and Snowden driving the 1963 Ford came last. I followed Price down Highway 19 and he turned left on to a gravel road. About a mile up the road he stopped and Snowden and I stopped behind him, with about a car length between each car. Before I could get out of the car[,] Wayne ran past my car to Price's car, opened the left rear door, pulled [Michael] Schwerner out of the car, spun him around so that Schwerner was standing on the left side of the road, with his back to the ditch and said[,] 'Are you that nigger lover' and Schwerner said[,] 'Sir, I know just how you feel.' Wayne had a pistol in his right hand, then shot Schwerner. Wayne then went back to Price's car and got [Andrew] Goodman, took him to the left side of the road with Goodman facing the road, and shot Goodman.

"When Wayne shot Schwerner, Wayne had his hand on Schwerner's shoulder. When Wayne shot Goodman, Wayne was standing within reach of him. Schwerner fell to the left so that he was laying along side the road. Goodman spun around and fell back toward the bank in back.

"At this time Jim Jordan said[,] '[S]ave one for me.' He then got out of Price's car and got Chaney out. I remember Chaney backing up, facing the road, and standing on the bank on the other side of the ditch and Jordan stood in the middle of the road and shot him. I do not remember how many times Jordan shot. Jordan then said[,] 'You didn't leave me anything but a nigger, but at least I killed me a nigger.' The three civil rights workers were then put into the back of their 1963 Ford wagon. I do not know who put the bodies in the car, but I only put Chaney's foot inside the car[.] Price then got into his car and drove back toward Highway 19. Wayne, Posey[,] and Jordan then got into the 1963 Ford and started up the road. Snowden, Arledge[,] and another person who I do not know the name of got into my car and we followed. I do not know the roads we took, but went through the outskirts of Philadelphia and

 to the [d]am site on [Olen Lovell] Burrage's property. When we arrived at the [d]am site someone said that the bulldozer operator was not there[,] and Wayne, Arledge[,] and I went in my car to find him. We drove out to a paved road and about a mile down the road.

Burrage

"We saw a 1957 Chevrolet, white and green, parked on the left side of the road. Wayne told me to stop[,] and we backed up to this car. Burrage and 2 other men were in the car. Wayne said that they [the bodies] were already down there [at the dam,] and Burrage said to follow them [Burrage's car]. I followed the 1957 Chevrolet back toward the [d]am site, taking a different road, until the Chevrolet stopped. Burrage said[,] '[I]t is just a little ways over there,' and Wayne and the bulldozer operator walked the rest of the way. The bulldozer operator was about 40 years old, 6 ft – 2 inches tall, slim built[,] and a white male. He was wearing khaki clothes. Arledge and I then followed Burrage and the other man back to Burrage's garage [NB: Burrage owned a towing company, and they went to the company garage]. The other man was a

66

white male, about 40 years old, 5 feet 8 or 9 inches tall, stocky built. Burrage's garage is on the road toward Philadelphia and he had tractors and trailer parked there. His house is across the road.

"We were there about 30 minutes when the other fellows came from the dam site in the 1963 Ford. Burrage got a glass gallon jug and filled it with gasoline to be used to burn the 1963 Ford car owned by the three civil rights workers. Burrage took one of the diesel trucks from under a trailer and said[,] 'I will use this to pick you up, no one will suspect a truck on the road this time at night.' It was then about 1:00 to 1:30 in the morning. Snowden, Arledge, Jordan, Wayne[,] and I then got into my car and we drove back toward Philadelphia. When we got to Philadelphia[,] a city patrol car stopped us and we got out. Sheriff [Lawrence A.] Rainey, Deputy Sheriff Price and the [c]ity [p]atrolman, who told us which way the civil rights workers were leaving town, got out of the patrol car. The patrolman was a white male, about 50 years old, 5 feet 8 to 9 inches, 160 lbs., and was wearing a uniform. This was about 2:00 [a.m.], June 22, 1964. I do not know his name, but I have met him before and would know him again.

Rainey

"We talked for 2 or 3 minutes and then someone said that we better not talk about this[,] and Sheriff Rainey said[,] 'I'll kill anyone who talks, even if it was my own brother.' We then got back into my car and drove back to Meridian and passed Posey's car[,] which was still parked along side the road. We did not stop and there was one or two men standing by Posey's car. We then kept going to Meridian. I took Wayne home, left Jordan and Snowden at Akin[']s Mobile Homes, took Arledge home and went home myself. I have read the above Statement, consisting of this and 9 other pages[,] and they are true and correct to the best of my knowledge and belief. I have signed my initials to the bottom of the first 9 pages and initial[ed] mistakes. No force threats or promises were made to induce me to make this statement."

Signed,
Horace Doyle Barnette

selective recall

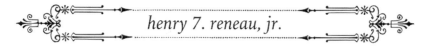

henry 7. reneau, jr.

We don't see things as they are; we see them as we are.
—Anaïs Nin

i remember my daughter's first smile

beneath a maternity ward Micky D heating lamp
recall as hauntingly familiar as battery acid
thrown into a public pool filled with black children

i remember wearing Levi 501s
RayBans
Black Panther / Huelga! / Power to The People! buttons
to my high school graduation
& the echo of a gunshot as the Messiah fell to hate

i remember first love's
tentative carousing puppy love
an emotion so deep i almost perished
like the soldier flogged, lynched & castrated
on the soil he fought to honor
his hand to heart pledging red / whiter / Blue(s)

i remember signs leading disciplined anger/: *I Am A Man!*

rocks & bottles flying
&
scalding words like rock salt in open wounds

the ill-mannered firehose
pushing & shoving men women   & children
&
snarling Gestapo hounds incited to hate

i remember . . .
Chewy the pimp at the Main Motel on Union Ave.

To live life, you take the bitter with the sweet

i remember . . .
that ear-ringin'   beam-me-up   boo-yah! sizzle
as the gorilla shifted
for better purchase on my back

i remember . . .
things were better yesterday   that weren't

Sanitation workers hold up "I Am a
Man" signs during the Memphis,
Tennessee, 1,300-man strike for better
pay, safety, equality, and benefits for
sanitation laborers, c. February 1968.

Stand-By

Stuart Stromin

Constable Hendrik Potgieter telephoned his wife at the South African Police Married Quarters and told her that the district of Alex was on fire, and that he would not be home for dinner. Everyone had been placed on stand-by. The permanent detail of the Alexander Riot Squad was already on patrol in the township, he told her, and it was likely that he would be on duty the whole night. She had already taken four pork chops from the freezer, but before she could begin quarreling, Potgieter slammed down the receiver.

Then he went into the hot back room of the Fairview police station to play darts with Sergeant Piet. There were five or six other policemen lounging around the room, as well. All the windows were wide open, and the officers had removed their caps and holsters. Andries Vermeulen, sitting on the narrow wooden bench against the brick wall, had unbuttoned his uniform so that his sweaty red belly hung over the belt of his trousers. He was talking loudly about the afternoon horseracing at Turffontein, but no one was listening. Everybody was dying for a beer.

The stand-by could last hours, and it was possible that they would not even be summoned at all. Fairview was the last police station in Johannesburg to report before the army intervened, and then, after them, the air force, though it was unlikely that things would go that far.

Potgieter lost five rand at darts to Sergeant Piet after only half an hour. The sergeant, who'd been stationed at Fairview for eleven years after being transferred from Krugersdorp, could hit the dartboard blindfolded. Potgieter gave up on the game, pushed a place for himself on the bench, and sat down beside Vermeulen.

"I don't know why they don't just let the *kaffirs* burn down the entire place," Potgieter grumbled, already tired of waiting.

Vermeulen said, "Alex is only a tinderbox. The whole of Soweto will be up in flames by this evening, mark my words. We won't get off duty for a week."

"But Jesus, Vermeulen, you've got a fat arse," Potgieter said. "Shift up a bit there, man. There's too many on this bench. Let that recruit sit on the floor."

The surly, young cadet at the end of the bench glanced up and said sullenly, "My arse is as important to me as yours is to you."

"Oh, is that what they teach you in the college, nowadays?" Potgieter said, but the junior officer did not reply.

Potgieter, a petty man with short legs, a pale complexion, and greasy brown hair, had been a constable for eight years, and there had been a number of assault charges against him, especially in the last seven months; he had never been convicted, but it was not worth provoking trouble. The young man stood casually and sauntered to the dartboard to watch Sergeant Piet aiming for bullseyes. But Potgieter's pockmarked cheeks were white with frustration.

Vermeulen started handing out 100-percent-guaranteed racing tips again, so—when the black sergeant from the C.I.D. office came in to fetch a docket—Potgieter asked Vermeulen to lend him a few rand. Vermeulen, caught in the homestretch of the two thousand meters, could not really refuse, and Potgieter sent the black detective to buy a six-pack of Lion lager from the off-license. His throat was as dry as a stick, Potgieter explained to Vermeulen.

Vermeulen was going to comment on what the warrant officer would say if he discovered beer on the premises, but then—thinking about one night shift he had spent with Potgieter when Fairview was short-staffed—he changed his mind and offered him a three-X mint. Potgieter took it, thanked him, and pretended to put it into his mouth, but Vermeulen knew that Potgieter would palm it and save it for later to disguise the smell of alcohol. He watched Potgieter from the corner of his eye, and sure enough, within ten seconds, Potgieter reached for his handkerchief, slipping the strong peppermint into his pocket. Vermeulen shook his head but said nothing. Potgieter wiped his damp forehead and shut his eyes, leaning back against the coolness of the brick wall with the soiled handkerchief still in his hand.

The warrant officer, tall and dapper, put his head through the doorway of the back room and told the men that they had better come and get issued with rifles and teargas canisters, in case they were called. Potgieter was the first in line for weapons, and, while he was signing the gun register, the warrant officer made a joke about how keen he was to go shooting.

"I just want to finish this and go home," Potgieter replied flatly.

"You won't go home for a fortnight," the warrant officer said.

Potgieter accidentally knocked over a teargas canister, which rolled beneath the warrant officer's desk. Cursing, the constable fumbled underneath the table on his hands and knees to retrieve it, and all the other policemen, waiting in line for ammunition, started jeering. They thought that he had cold feet. But when he stood up squarely with the threatening cylinder in his hand and said, "Who wants to try it?" they were instantly silent.

He returned to the narrow bench in the back room, sitting with his R1 rifle upright between his legs. Perspiration trickled down his back, and he knew it would leave marks on his uniform. His wife had done the washing on Wednesday morning; he would have to wear the sweat-stained clothing until the unrest was over. He hoped the rioting would not last as long as it did during the previous outbreak. If it rained, the rioting would have to cease, the fires would die, the stand-by would be canceled, and he would be allowed to go home. He would still be able to have meat for dinner, if only it would rain.

But the sky was cloudless for miles, and the sun beat down oppressively.

One by one, the other policemen came back into the room, leaning their rifles in a long row against the wall. Sergeant Piet had been issued with a hand-machine carbine, and the young trainee had to show him how it worked. Despite the regulations in the standing orders, the old sergeant never carried a gun. *Give me a solid truncheon any time* was his motto; there was nothing a *kaffir* understood as well as a smack on the head, he used to say.

But Potgieter had no dislike for firearms. He had even taken his pistol home one evening. He didn't think he was as invincible as Sergeant Piet thought of himself; one never knew when a gun would come in handy. He had decided not to make a habit of carrying a police-issued weapon, however, because of the complications that would arise if he were caught with it off-duty. But he'd buy his own gun as soon as he could afford it. He promised himself a revolver, which would not jam in an emergency. There would be no difficulty about obtaining a license because he could complete the police clearance form himself; all he needed was the official date-stamp, and that would be easy to get.

He stroked the smooth metal of the rifle.

The game of darts began once more, though by this time the players had lost interest in the dartboard itself and were trying to peg the darts into the printed documents on the noticeboard. A dart went into Potgieter's name on the duty register. No one took it out, and he stood up himself to remove it. Then he sat down again and flung the dart back into the board. It went into a list of murder suspects from the police gazette.

Two of the younger constables clowned around, making paper airplanes from the charge sheets, but Sergeant Piet told them to cut it out when one of them knocked over, first, one rifle, and then, the whole stack. The barrels clattered to the floor noisily, and the two offenders stooped sheepishly to pick them up again. Potgieter still held his weapon securely between his thighs. The barrel of the rifle was cool and dry on the bright, sticky afternoon.

Vermeulen sat down wearily beside Potgieter again, the wooden bench creaking beneath Vermeulen's weight. "I suppose the boy got lost," he said, referring to the black detective.

Potgieter snapped, "Lose yourself, Vermeulen. You'll get your money back." He struck the butt of his rifle on the ground for emphasis.

Vermeulen shrugged. "Heaven help us if a black detective ever has to find a suspect, never mind a six-pack."

"Man, don't you ever use Right Guard?" Potgieter said, looking for friction.

But Vermeulen, who had worked with Potgieter that one time on night shift, said nothing. It was hard to forget waiting with Potgieter in the dark patrol van for three chilly hours one winter night, parked outside the South African Police Married Quarters, watching a window on the third floor.

Potgieter shifted on the rigid bench, uncomfortable with the silence from Vermeulen. Potgieter eyed him suspiciously. Then the warrant officer, who had been talking to a major from Randwood police, came in again and told them that a Hippo had been sent into the township. Potgieter thought how ridiculous it was to send an anti-landmine vehicle, designed for the bush, into a township. Things must be drastic. The warrant officer said that they should be prepared to leave for Alexander soon.

Tensely, the young trainee sat down on the bench again and unwrapped a box of Benson and Hedges. He crumpled the cellophane and threw it onto the floor beneath the bench, kicking it with the back of his shoe. He tapped the bottom of the box nervously and took out a cigarette, tossing it into his mouth with a well-practiced technique. He offered Vermeulen a cigarette, as well, and the heavyset policeman said yes. Potgieter ordered the recruit to pick up the paper he had dropped; this was a police station, not a *kaffir-kraal*.

The cadet stood and went to the door, expecting to be called at any second.

But the Fairview police had to wait another two hours and twenty minutes in the heat, before the warrant officer eventually returned and told Sergeant Piet to sign the register and to start up the big, blue truck. The sergeant threw a final dart into the board. It landed on the triple thirteen, which was unlucky for some, and he went to fetch the ignition keys from the charge office.

Potgieter stood, scowling. The black detective had not returned with the beers or the money during the entire afternoon, and now it was time to go. But he would get hold of the detective during night shift and show him a thing or two.

The cadet took a last draw on his fifth cigarette and stamped it out beneath his heel. Vermeulen got to his feet and buttoned his tunic, and they all went outside.

A squad of black policemen in green camouflage uniform, looking as tough as soldiers, was waiting stiffly in a single-file line in the courtyard. One could hear the heavy crack of their shiny brown boots on the ground as the men snapped to attention. They all bundled into the back of the truck, holding their immaculate rifles smartly across their chests. Four of the white policemen, including

74

Potgieter and Vermeulen, squished into the front cab. The other whites went with the warrant officer in the new squad car.

They had to drive through the impatient traffic of Johannesburg to get to Alexander because the shantytown lay squeezed between the elegant suburbs, like a huge servants' quarters. The other motorists honked at the police cars. The warrant officer authorized Sergeant Piet to use the flashing blue light, and a traffic warden sped ahead of them, blaring his siren. It was urgent now.

Disturbing the tranquility of the suburbs, they progressed steadily. Idle housewives on the way home from the supermarket or the hairdresser peered at the convoy from behind Mercedes-Benz steering wheels. A blonde in a sportscar raised her trendy sunglasses to see more clearly as the convoy took a shortcut down a quiet suburban street.

A gardener, watering a flowerbed, dropped his hose and fled, freeing the rubber pipe to splash sweeping arcs of water like a trapped puff-adder spraying poison. In his panic to escape the police, the gardener almost stumbled into the swimming pool in the yard before he dived through the hedge. But the four policemen in the cab just laughed. There was no time to stop for a simple pass offender, who imagined that the entire brigade had been activated for his capture.

Two white schoolboys on bicycles, from one of the private schools in the neighborhood, stuck their fingers in the air in an obscene gesture. They shouted, "Oink! Oink!" and Potgieter wanted to jump out with a flat hand, but Sergeant Piet told him that there would be enough schoolboys for him as soon as they got to Alex. Smoke could be seen rising over the tin roofs of the township in the distance.

They passed a fleet of big, green PUTCO buses, parked, empty. Every window was smashed, and three of the huge public transportation vehicles were black with ash and soot. One of the bus drivers, sitting hunched on the charred steps of his wrecked vehicle, spat on the ground as the police convoy headed past the smoldering buses in the direction of the rough dirt roads of the shattered township.

Through the haze of dust and heat and buzzing flies, they saw the untidy cluster of patrol vans, squad cars, and motorcycles. Tall antennae stretched into the dry air. Behind the barricades, the big Bedford trucks with SAP license plates and limp canvas canopies, and the massive hulking Hippos, like terrifying machines from a science-fiction feature, loomed threateningly. Shield-like wire mesh was fitted securely over the windshields and headlamps on all the land rovers, and in tight cages German Shepherds were snarling. Hot saliva dripping from their jaws, the dogs scratched continually on the wire confines, hungry to run. Military webbing, crackling wirelesses, and crates of ammunition were strewn about. And, everywhere, full of listlessness and tension, there were platoons of tired and bitter men.

The Fairview police could smell the smoky air as they neared, and the acidic trace of teargas burned and stung their eyes. Vermeulen started coughing and quickly rolled up the window of the cab, but his colleagues, pressured by the stifling heat, demanded that he open it again. He had to cough and splutter till they jerked to a halt. He tumbled from the cab, heaving asthmatically, and sat down gasping on the pavement. Potgieter regarded him in disgust, and, hearing an officer calling, went to join the ranks immediately.

A long, sloppy row of burly men, armed with wooden batons, leather *sjamboks*, pistols, rifles, and grenades, stood scratching and fidgeting expectantly. Most of them were dressed in loose green-khaki camouflage, and, for a moment, Potgieter felt out of place in his more formal royal-blue uniform, with his stiff peaked cap and his brass buttons. He felt like an office clerk, and everyone could see that he had just arrived. He scraped his polished shoes in the dust, looking down to avoid the glare of the sun. He dug for Vermeulen's triple-X mint in the pocket of his trousers and put it into his mouth. Sweat poured off his face. A smooth-shaven lieutenant, with cloth stars on his shoulders, called for attention. Mumbling and swearing, the men gradually stilled.

A short, dumpy colonel, in khaki and dark sunglasses, stepped stolidly before them. "These people are breaking the laws of this country," he yelled hoarsely at his subordinates, "under the provisions of the Riotous Assemblies Act." He paced up and down along the line, his swagger stick tucked under his arm. "They have had plenty of fair warning to disband. There are no innocent bystanders."

A stone, the size of a man's fist, fell from the air. It landed just short of the officer. He looked around, down the narrow dusty street, to see a ragged crowd of men, women, and children advancing resolutely toward the barricades. Some waved crudely lettered banners, some waved solid *knobkierries* and flaming torches, and they were all chanting slogans or singing freedom songs.

The members of the permanent detail of the Riot Squad pulled gas masks over their faces at once.

Another stone fell, and then, a half-brick. A liter-sized bottle collided against one of the squad cars. Shards of glass showered all over the place.

"They are all under arrest!" the red-faced colonel bawled furiously. "Every last one of them." The pace of the approaching mob quickened, more clods rained down, and the commanding officer struck his stick impatiently into his palm. "Go!" he roared.

The policemen charged forward, flinging the first barrage of teargas into the pack. Huge clouds of white gas billowed, fumes breaking the cornered crowd. The dogs were unleashed. Placards fell to the ground, and, as the police rushed ahead, the frenzied rioters fled in all directions, screaming and weeping from the pain of the chemical clouds. Police cadets with sjamboks whipped the retreaters as they ran; anyone who stumbled was pounced upon immediately, surrounded by a cluster of men, and dragged away to the patrol vans, amid screams and struggles.

Potgieter saw a powerful sergeant swing his arm and strike a middle-aged woman in the teeth with a wooden club. She howled as blood spurted from her mouth, and he beat her again across the side of the head.

A dozen scuffles were breaking around him. Men were using the butts of their rifles like solid lances, ramming their opponents in the face or in the stomach as they clashed. Teargas grenades were lobbed nonstop, the wind catching the acrid mist and blinding the rioters so that they could not even see the onset of the next attack.

Two thickset officers were punching an old man. Some of the younger constables had drawn their pistols.

A monstrous Hippo hurtled down a street, oblivious to the stones rattling against the steel chassis, and panicky rebels leaped out of its path, tumbling right into the dust. Roaring engines, growls, shouts, and caterwauling grew louder and wilder, and, sizzling beneath the noise of anarchy, was the crackle of fire.

Where the dogs were loosed, an instant arc of empty space appeared. Encouraged by their trainers, the animals leaped upon the slower members of the throng, fangs tearing into flesh. As the dogs converged upon each new victim, the mob swept into another position, anger swelling more intensely all the while.

Rocks and bottles fell steadily. Now and then, the containers would burst into flames as they hit the ground, and the policemen had to dodge any debris from the sky, rapidly pacing backward if necessary. Then they would storm forward again into the chaos, even more violently than before. Bullets punctured the racket of the crowd in sporadic bursts.

A brave youth in tattered overalls kicked a hissing teargas canister back toward the policemen. Some constables retreated, and a few of the rioters started advancing again.

"Fire!" urged the colonel, a few yards away from Potgieter, with a machine carbine under each arm.

Potgieter, who had been on stand-by all day, raised his rifle.

A teenaged boy was coming toward Potgieter with a rock in each hand. The officer could see the eyes of the adolescent clearly, despite all the smoke and confusion and fury. He saw reckless flames raging in the youth's eyes, and he saw flames and smoke climbing from the crumbling rooftops of Alexander and swirling high in the sweltering South African sky, and he knew that now the rioting and the fighting were only beginning.

His arm steady, he took aim.

A helicopter flapped overhead, and Potgieter knew that now the whole of Soweto was alight, as Vermeulen had predicted, and that all through the country the police were out, and the army was out, and that on the edge of every city and every village in the torn republic, the bonfires were burning, and they would burn stubbornly until twilight and then deep into the night. He had been on stand-by all day, and he knew as the teenager advanced, that he would be on stand-by 24 hours a day for the rest of the summer.

And in his blasted heart, Hendrik Potgieter of SAP Fairview knew that, for every second of every night of the pitiless nights ahead, while he was being smothered with the dust and the heat and the rotten stench of death that was already rising, his delicate wife, Anita, would be lying in the arms of the manager of a Ford dealership. He could see the proud, blue eyes of the handsome Englishman as sharply as he could see the sour reflection of fury in the eyes of the young black martyr, as he squeezed the trigger.

(Above) Mounted police in Bekkersdal, South Africa, May 6, 2014.

(Right) Policemen in Natal, South Africa, who wore no shoes with their uniforms, 1890.

For Samuel Ajayi Crowther

Ayokunle Falomo

At 12, captured   along with the rest of your kin
        Reminds me of   my youngest brother who, newly
12, swears this means   he is a man. I think of him, two
    Years before, walking into   a country that is not his. Assimilation
A white cloth, his mouth   is wiped clean of my mother's
    Tongue. I speak in Yoruba   to my brother, and he responds
In English. I have always wondered   how your name (especially
    Your last) isn't like mine, Crowther   even though they taught us that
You spoke in the same tongue.   I thought once to buy a shovel for,
    Yes, in this new country, I wanted to   dig a hole deep enough to
Engulf home. But I still have this name, traceable. My American
    Doesn't know how to walk into   Anywhere without leaving

A trail of blood that'll lead Everyone to where   I tried to bury
My Nigerian. I am Nigerian   but not in the way my father is.
    My youngest brother is, too,   but not in the way I am. I am
A man, too, but I do not think I am   like my father is. Did you,
    Like my brother, think yourself a man at 12?   When your mother,
A descendant of an actual king,   birthed you, did she
    Ever fear the day   your body would mistake a slave-ship
For a throne? Ajayi, shall I call you   by this, this name that belongs
    Also to my father's father or by the English   name my father, Joshua
And my mother, Ruth   did not bless me with? Did you
    Know this name of yours means born   face-down? Did you
Assume the posture of supplication   from the womb? Samuel,

This name of yours means God has heard.   And wasn't it fitting
    That you'd be a gong?   That you'd wring their holy book
Into this language   they couldn't scrub clean
    From your tongue? Even if   the whole mouth
Swallows an entire   tongue, the aftertaste of loss still lingers.
    Crowther, did you know your name   was derived from a stringed
Instrument that is now   archaic? But here you are—
    Echo loud and in tune   with the heartbeat
Of a boy you do not know   by name
    And who is, too,   though under different circumstances, far
Away from home—   even more than a century
    After a stroke stole the last note   from your throat.

Samuel Ajayi Crowther,
Nigerian linguist and first
African Anglican bishop of
West Africa, c. 1888.

How I Was Captured into Slavery

Samuel Ajayi Crowther

Letter written in Fourah Bay (a neighborhood in Freetown, Sierra Leone), on February 22, 1837, to Reverend Williams Jowett, then-secretary of the Church Missionary Society (all sic).

R ev. and dear Sir,

As I think it will be interesting to you to know something of the conduct of Providence in my being brought to this Colony, where I have the happiness to enjoy the privilege of the Gospel, I give you a short account of it, hoping I may be excused if I should prove rather tedious in some particulars.

I suppose [sometime] about the commencement of the year 1821, I was in my native country, enjoying the comforts of father and mother, and affectionate love of brothers and sisters. From this period I must date the unhappy, but which I am now taught, in other respects, to call blessed day, which I shall never forget in my life.

I call it unhappy day, because it was the day in which I was violently turned out of my father's house, and separated from relations; and in which I was made to experience what is called to be in slavery—with regard to its being called blessed, it being the day which Providence had marked out for me to set out on my journey from the land of heathenism, superstition, and vice, to a place where His Gospel is preached.

For some years, war had been carried on in my Eyo (Oyo) country, which was always attended with much devastation and bloodshed; the women, such men as had surrendered or were caught, with the children, were taken captives. The enemies who carried on th[is] war were principally the Oyo Mahomendans, with whom my country abounds—with the Foulahs (Fulbe), and such foreign slaves as had escaped from their owners. Joined together, making a formidable force of about 20,000, who annoyed the whole country. They had no other employment but selling slaves to the Spaniards and Portuguese on the coast.

The morning in which my town, Ocho-gu (Osogun), shared the same fate which many others had experienced, was fair and delightful; and most of the inhabitants were engaged in their respective occupations. We were preparing breakfast without any apprehension; when, about 9 o'clock a.m.[,] a [rumor] was spread in the town that the enemies had approached with intentions of hostility. It was not long after when they had almost surrounded the town, to prevent any escape of the inhabitants; the town being rudely fortified with a wooded fence, about four miles in circumference, containing about 12,000 inhabitants, which would produce 3,000 fighting men. The inhabitants not being duly prepared, some not being at home; those who were, having about six gates to defend, as well as many weak places about the fence to guard against, and, to say in a few words, the men being surprised, and therefore confounded—the enemies entered the town after about three or four hours' resistance.

Here a most sorrowful scene imaginable was to be witnessed! —women, some with three, four, six children clinging to their arms, with the infant on their backs, and such baggage as they could carry on their heads, running as far as they could through prickly shrubs, which, hooking their blies and other loads, drew them down from the heads of the bearers. While they found [it] impossible to go along with their loads, they [endeavored] only to save themselves and their children: even this was impracticable with those who had many children to care for.

While they were [endeavoring] to disentangle themselves from the ropy shrubs, they were overtaken and caught by the enemies with a noose of rope thrown over the neck of every individual, to be led in the manner of goats tied together, under the drove of one man. In many cases a family was violently divided between three or four enemies, who each led his [captive] away, to see one another no more.

Your humble servant was thus caught—with his mother, two sisters (one an infant about ten months old), and a cousin—while [endeavoring] to escape in the manner above described. My load consisted in nothing else than my bow, and five arrows in the quiver, the bow I had lost in the shrub, while I was extricating myself, before I could think of making any use of it against my enemies. The last view I had of my father was when he came from the fight, to give us the signal to flee: he entered into our house which was [burned] some time back for some [offense] given by my father's adopted son. Hence[,] I never saw him [my father] more—Here I must take thy leave, unhappy, comfortless father!—I learned, some time afterward, that he was killed in another battle.

Our conquerors were Oyo Mahomendans, who led us away through the town. On our way, we met a man badly wounded on the head struggling between life and death. Before we got half-way through the town, some Foulahs (Fulbe), among the enemies themselves, hostilely separated my cousin from our number, here also I must take thy leave, my fellow captive cousin! His mother was living in another village. The town on fire—the houses being built with mud, some about twelve feet from the ground with high roofs, in square forms, of different dimensions and spacious areas; several of these belonged to one man, adjoined to, with passage communicating with each other. The flame was very high.

We were led by my grandfather's house, already desolate; and in a few minutes after, we left the town to the mercy of the flame, never to enter or see it [anymore]. Farewell, a place of my birth, the playground of my childhood, and the place which I thought would be the repository of my mortal body in its old age.

We were now out of Osogun, going into a town called Isehin (Iseyin), the [rendezvous] of the enemies, about twenty miles from my town. On the way we saw our grandmother at a distance, with about three or four of my cousins taken with her, for a few minutes: she was missed through the crowd to see her no more. Several other captives were held in the same manner as we were: grandmothers, mothers, children, and cousins were all led captives. O sorrowful prospect! The aged women were to be greatly pitied, not being able to walk so fast as their children and grandchildren; they were often threatened with being put to death upon the spot, to get rid of them, if they would not go fast as others, and they [the kidnappers] [were] often as wicked in their practice as in their words. O pitiful sight! Whose heart would not bleed to have seen this? Yes, such is the state of barbarity in the heathen land. Evening came on; and coming to a spring of water[,] we drank a great quantity; which served us for breakfast, with a little parched corn and dried meat previously prepared by our victors for themselves.

Samuel Ajayi Crowther was resettled in Freetown, Sierra Leone, depicted here in a watercolor-and-ink drawing from the mid-19th century, after the British Naval Patrol intercepted the slave ship that carried him in April 1822. One of the buildings in the drawing is a compound for liberated Africans.

Words in parentheses are clarifications from the transcription of J. F. Ade-Ajayi in his book A Patriot to the Core: Bishop Ajayi Crowther, *the source of this letter, or from* The Nigerian News, *who reprinted the letter in 2016. Words in brackets are clarifications from* Footnote *editors.*

Woman of Breasts

Mary Jane Panke

Nangeli, I love you before I know
your story. I have dreams,
poems about breasts in silver
cups, tears 200 years after
the tax collectors come to your home
with metal scales, tell you to uncover,
weigh your breasts in a pan.
Because of your caste, because you
drape yourself at the market, you
must pay *mulakkaram*, the price
for the space and weight of you.
The men at your door arrive
to touch you with their eyes, punish you
with their laws. You stand undeterred
and ask them to wait. I imagine
your perfect hands poised until you
carefully remove your scarf, take
each breast in your palm,
calmly, cleanly, cut it from your body,
and hand them over on a leafy plate.
I see you fall on your knees, hear
the screams of women, your husband
broken and burned. I see men recoil
from your sacrifice as they flee
your humble door where you
bleed and die, your widening eyes
boring into their lie, that one human being
is worth less than another.
Nangeli of *mulachiparambu*,
"the land where woman of breasts lived,"
I remember you and say your name. Nangeli.

There is no historical
evidence or record of
Nangeli, but you can
scan to learn more
about her legend.

Jubilo Done Pass

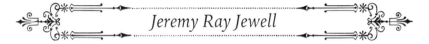

Jeremy Ray Jewell

New Bedford, Massachusetts, 1868.

D avid, my friend, I am finally setting about the task of writing to you that story I had been referring to. As you know I'm not one to wade into the morass of politics these days. I have my positions, and no one has ever cared about them. When the South asserts its "rights," we rage, we gnash our teeth. When they behave in the same manner, well, we asserted our own "rights," and talked of secession in New England. When we wanted, we marched into Canada or Virginia, and then when the Southerner wanted to take Florida, even all of Mexico, then even Lincoln could act as to claim the peaceable high ground of a Quaker. And what does Sergeant Randolph think? I think to hell with everything west of New Bedford. Because what's good for us we'll keep, right, David? Purge the sins that mimicked ours, but let us and ours alone in peace. On our New England coast, our eyes ever Eastward, blessed to be warmed thence from without the howling wilderness that we still pretend is behind our backs, there where Worcester sits. That is why I am living as I am these days. I guess Florida will still be part of our Union a hundred years from now. Still, it won't be part of my world tomorrow nor the next day, nor ever again, God willing. So let us begin. For now, we know our goal: to tell a good story. That is all. That's usually the best excuse to go off to war, as it is, for at least you know you will get a good story out of it.

At that time, of course, I was Sergeant Randolph, 4th Massachusetts Cavalry, 2nd Battalion. I left Boston at the end of winter in 1864 on a steamer. As we approached the coast of South Carolina, I searched for a glimpse of Fort Sumter, that mythical rock from whence this sad revolution began, to see that brick which had come hurtling through our window three years prior. I was looking out to the horizon thus when a crewman spoke to me: "You'll get where you're going, to be sure. . . . 't may not be Carolina, but you'll get there. Jus' over a month ago, she took on a rebel steamer whilst en route from New Orleans. Turned right aroun' an' took all the booty down to Key West. An' again, there's always the deep blue down there, right? Plenty a'places to go besides where you're headed, plenty a'places." I declare, he spoke thus, then simply departed in silence. However, we did finally arrive in Hilton Head. Throughout April and May, we were assigned to picket, mostly. Not much use in a cavalry thusly employed. The negroes on the island spoke of experiences since fleeing. Or rather often, since being fled from, as the home of many was on a number of these islands. In the retreat to the interior, the rebels had burned the negroes' quarters and anything else of value to them, causing a mass of them to accumulate on the islands. The general conditions of these people in the waning days of their captivities were varied, but all involved danger, violence, loss. As the war had progressed, this wandering band of refugees expanded, forcing Sherman to move them from island to island. Never had they been gathered before in such great number, and wherever they went, they struggled with the conditions of war. As you have heard, twice as many of us died from sickness in camp as from battle, and to these same trials were also put the negro refugee.

In June, my company was relocated to Jacksonville, Florida. There, I met another curious variety of wandering man, the Southern Unionist. Jacksonville on a whole was fairly amicable toward our presence, despite our visits being frequent and our welcome long overstayed. Doubtlessly this owed much to the migration and expulsion of rebel loyalists from the coast to Lake City in the interior, though as they went, they were replaced with Union loyalists coming thither. There in Jacksonville, I met such a man from farther west who had lost all his estate to a Sequestration Act. Before that, however, he narrowly escaped with his life as a member of a cabal that had been mostly put to the sword by their countrymen. His affiliation hadn't come to light until such a time when, as he said, his kind had "b'come too valuable ta hang, as they'd sooner throw your corpse at the en'my." He escaped his ranks and made it to Jacksonville, where the residents did not know what to make of him and others of the sort. The city folks were not particularly staunch Confederates themselves, but as they saw it, it was in their nature. They could not see what it was in the nature of these poor country folks to make them that way, and so they viewed them with distrust. All the more so as they arrived empty-handed. I tell you, these wandering souls will all need accounting for in the wake of these travails. I can't see how the Government will manage with these things, but to either let such people turn to death or disorder.

From Jacksonville, we made a number of raids targeting the railroads. In late July, we first encountered the name "Middleburg." At that time, we were met by Colored Troops, who spoke still of Fort Pillow, in a place called Mandarin. The graybacks were across the river here, where two of our vessels had been sunk. As a result, some infantry from home were ordered to obliterate all the domiciles along the water there. I questioned this, aware that there were a number of native Unionists located there, but it was practical. Now, three months later, we were to start straight into that hornet's nest. I looked out and assessed the river, as wide as Boston Harbor or wider. As wide as Buzzards Bay, even, and riddled with submarine torpedoes. I wondered what might greet us on the other side. "The poor bastards," said my fellow sergeant, Shadrack, as we stood before where the *Maple Leaf* had sunken, "they'd planted so much cotton they'd not much room for corn and potatoes. And it was expensive cotton, like they'd had on the islands. It's a loss, to be sure." We headed by steamer across to that other shore, past ruined homes, and up the Black Creek . . . aptly named for its brackishness and our dread, both. Disembarking, we marched through forest and farm and on to Middleburg for the first time. We were repulsed by the rebels in that town. The Colored Troops continued into the interior, while the 4th Cavalry quit that bank and returned east. Eventually, we went forth to Gainesville and were joined by a loosely organized amalgamation of Florida Unionists and a regiment of mounted infantry from Ohio. We'd entered the town square there, with townsfolk looking upon us from the windows like curious hens. Ever so briefly we stared into their eyes like the first stars of twilight, trying to decipher their portents, and then suddenly we were trounced upon. This was a good deal more frightening and awful than skirmishing and fighting off sleep and ticks at an outpost. I made it back to Jacksonville, where I survived the remainder of the hot, miserable summer. This was war . . . mostly waiting and drilling.

I passed much of my time in camp with Sergeant Shadrack, of Dorchester, whose family was in the business of pears back home. He spoke well and made a good companion, although I could not quite see us holding each other's company in our old lives. We were provided with much entertainment by Corporal Leigh, the Irishman, who cut a jovial figure loving to drink and dance. I had become a sort of confidante to him, both from the necessity of our relative ranks and owing to the displeasure that he often engendered among others just as drunk as him. He had once begun to sing "The Battle Cry of Freedom" alongside his musicians, enjoining the participation of his crew of teamsters and such. He sang, with an arm around a young Floridian, "We will welcome to our numbers the loyal, true, and brave, shouting the battle cry of—?" He put his finger to the Floridian's chest with a pause, forcing the man to smile nervously. "—Freeeedom!" sang Leigh. "And although he may be poor—" Someone among the mass of the other corporals' crews had cried out "IRISH!" over that last word. Visibly aggrieved but undeterred, Leigh continued, ". . . he shall never be a slave. . . ." I tell you, at that moment you could see the poor man's heart on his sleeve. "Down with the traitor," he sang, "and up with the star!" Another corporal interrupted, "And what were you before they were traitors? The Village Yankee?" Laughter issued from all corners. I became aware that I needed to intercept the mounting rage of the Irishman. Since then, he afforded me great loyalty as First Corporal, which is always important.

At long last we were moving again, back down the broad St. John's River, past Mandarin, to a place called Magnolia. It was a winter place for Northerners more monied than ourselves, complete with a boarding house, billiard saloon, livery stable, and a handful of residences. We stepped ashore there in an area thickly shaded with large oak and Spanish moss, yet feeling in some sense as though we'd just stepped into a corner of Boston Common preserved apart from us. Together with soldiers from Connecticut and Ohio and two colored regiments, we encamped on a land called Magnolia Springs, somewhere near where, in the last century, the British governor's plantation stood. "What good fortune," quipped Shadrack. "Just the reputation we want to inherit." It was an ominous reflection. Though such folks as remained in Magnolia did not seem hostile to us as we erected our earthen fortifications, particularly since we brought with us kerosene and other things, we gradually were made aware of some troubling local lore. Apart from the Confederate lines, and against the wariness of a portion of the populace, there had risen a fanatical confederacy of guerrillas in those parts. These were led first by a planter named Huston, who had ultimately been captured and died. Now, however, there was rumored to be a second, more fanatical planter by the name of Hines. The people around Magnolia all were terrified of him and had apparently been so inclined long before the crisis of the Union. We heard all manner of tales, from cannibalism to shamanism. The people had taken to calling his group "Seminoles" while holding their namesakes in higher esteem. Through all the whispers, a series of aspects buoyed to the surface that were more substantiated than others. First was that he had held a longstanding erotic liaison with an adolescent negress in his estate, which also possessed a contrary paternal aspect. All of which is to say that it was disturbing to the folks of the area on a multiplicity of levels. Second, Hines had allegedly dismissed his wife to St. Augustine following the rebel victory at Ocean Pond the year before, declaring his intention to kill her were she ever to return. Third, it was said that Hines possessed a guard of his own negroes with a fanatical, near-religious devotion to him. And fourth, it was said that he had continued to win the support of the most dejected whites of the bush and swamps, with whom he was now hiding out like Osceola himself.

Shadrack and I brought these reports to our captain, Gomes. Captain Gomes was a quiet man, but from what we deduced, he had come from Portuguese stock off some fishing island back home. He had a slightly darker complexion and a long beard that he liked to hold in one fist as he stood. Captain Gomes assured us that he was aware of the rumors, but that he had no orders to act, nor any reliable information on the thing. Together with Shadrack, I also came to know a Dr. Herman Ichabod Culpeper in Magnolia, a man educated at Chapel Hill and initially pleasant to speak to. Dr. Culpeper confirmed that Hines and his "Seminoles" were a danger to the town. "How do you know?" I asked him. The Carolina doctor stood among his foreign bottles and books in his tin-roof cabin and replied, "Well, Sergeant Randolph, I've treated Hines. I been out to his plantation a number of times 'fore he left it, and if there's anythin' I can be sure of, it is his tenacity. Hines' plantation was never the South. It was only ever Hines' plantation, and nothin' more. What went on in that dominion did not belong to our Southern civilization. It belonged to the kingdom of Hines, alone, if not also to the Devil. Florida is still wilderness, Sergeant. It never was the frontiers of the West, which were touched by civilization and transport long before the spiritual children of Barbados made it out there with their rice, cotton, sugar. Many a man has come here to Florida to do more than profit within respectable society. They've come here to step outside of it." Shadrack and I looked at one another. "What about you, Doctor?" asked Shadrack. Culpeper cut into a swamp cabbage with his knife. "I come here like any good American, sirs. I come fer profit, an' nothin' else."

We waited in Magnolia, expecting at some point to ride toward Middleburg again. At this time, Corporal Leigh and the colored sentry Cyrus had taken a liking to the number "Kingdom Coming," and would sing it on and off all day throughout the camp, both with and without musicians. "Say, darkies, have you seen the massa, wit' the mustache on his face? Go 'long the road some time this mornin', like he gone to leave the place?" I couldn't help but think of Hines, the disgrace of fleeing, and what a man might do who knew no greater disgrace than that. "The massa run, ha, ha! The darkey stay, ho, ho! It mus' be now the kingdom comin', an' de year of Jubilo!" As I was hearing their voices ring in the distance, Shadrack came and threw open the canvas of my tent. "Come," he said, summoning me to follow him to a stand of trees on the edge of the camp. There in the pines stood a desperate-looking man covered in filth. At Shadrack's urging, he spoke, "I know y'all cain git inta Middleburg well enough. I got y'all some infamation on the way y'all's goin' down yonder, where Halsey's place got this ol' overseer that ain't leave. He's stayin' there ta call 'em back in town once he sees y'all comin', but I know where he at." I spoke to Shadrack, "Have you told the Captain?" Shadrack looked at the man and said, "There's a condition on your information, isn't there?"

The man looked at me, said, "Sir, I'm George Nowlins. Me an' my wife, Winnie, live by Magnolia Mills. Sir, when y'all done take the Mississippi, you know they tells us we need to drive all our cattle up to Savannah an' Charl'ston, an' they say there's a commissary district callin' fer *three thousand head a cattle*, an' I don' know what to do! I says, 'No, I'mma poor cracker, I cain't,' an' then they send the Cow Cavalry out ta me an' scare me hal' ta deaf wi' rifles, sayin' I been drivin' 'em heffers to the Fed'rals an' St. Augustine, and they gone take all I got iffin my cows cain't join the Confed'racy. They did this, an' then right 'fore y'all come down here, the gov'ment come an' say they's takin' my pigs. I say, 'Okay, okay, yes, an' I'll starf. That's the idea, huh?' I tells you, I raised a stink. . . . I'mma marked man, sir. I know the folks in Magnolia are all patriots, sir. I know they's glad to be back home wi' y'all, but you know a patriot is a diff'rent thang than a Tory, an' I ain't 'bout to give up now that y'all fin'ly come ta help us." He reached into his trousers pocket with a quivering hand and produced a scrap of paper. "See this?" he asked, holding it out. "I cain't read, but I know what it says. It says, 'Thanks fer the eggs, we'll be back fer them hens.' Sir, iffin I'm gone live, it'll be wi' the Union, an' any which'a way besides, I'mma die. But they cain make thangs worse fer me. Please, sir, iffin I help y'all, please make sure Uncle Sam gone protect his nephew George!"

I took the scrap of paper from the man and examined it. "Mr. Nowlins," I began, "brother Nowlins, my family, too, has had problems with foxes 'round the henhouse. Welcome home, brother Nowlins." The man shed a tear as I put my hand on his shoulder and squeezed. Shadrack and I conferred with one another on how to broach the subject to the Captain in such a way that would not betray Mr. Nowlins, and then went through with the plan.

Soon after that arrived the negroes from Holly Point and Laurel

Grove. They had fled amid the disarray on the night when the infantry had torched the houses along the riverfront. They swam from there down to the ruined Huston plantation and were subsequently joined by others as they passed through Hibernia. "You hear dat, Sergeant Randolph?" laughed Leigh. "De contryband says he's from *Hibernia*—dat's Ireland! Fancy seein' you down here, brother!" His tone was lightly sardonic. "It was your brother in the big house, actually," I said, matter-of-factly. This constituted a miniature crisis for us, as the hungry townsfolk in Magnolia already surely looked at us as a strain, nevermind several dozen negroes. They came down to us across the mouth of Black Creek, swimming across at night, and said they had observed some small band patrolling around there . . . enough to present them a danger were they not under our protection, and swimming to us had revealed their presence, they said. The leader of the group, a man identifying as the father of several others, spoke to me: "We hafta tell you, sir. . . . We 'spect they's gone kill us." His eyes stared wide and steady, straight into mine. Impulsively, I tried to look away but could not. Consequently, I presented their case to Captain Gomes. "We won't send them up to Black Creek, but they can't stay here, and we can't give them provisions," he said, holding his beard. "We understand it is our duty, but we are speaking about what is in our capacity. We suggest they stay beyond the branch to our north, where we may afford them some security by our proximity." I nodded.

I awoke late that night to what I thought were distant screams, followed by a guttural groan. I sat up and stepped outside. "Possums," said a wagoner who stood among the camp rows, evidently startled, as well. Beside him stood the colored sentry named Cyrus whose attention remained fixed on the darkness. I returned to my tent and sat worried until the dawn, when I rode out to the branch with Leigh and another of my corporals. We crossed through the dense woods and palmettoes and then waded through the water to the other side. There, in one large mass, we found the refugees. They had been mutilated and disfigured, blood shining brightly on their brown skin, reflecting the slashes of light bearing down through the canopy above. I couldn't retain the contents of my stomach, and vomited right there. The other corporal, a man I nearly lost in Gainesville, began heaving, as well. "Where's the honor in that?" he whined. Leigh looked on. "You recken dey cut his nose off before dey killed him or after?" he asked. "Or maybe dey cut his nose off, an' he killed hisself?" Some of these were Huston's slaves. I could think of no motive without him around any longer, nor any motive for such brutality in general. This could not have been done by a small number. It required for the entire group to be overpowered and desecrated all at the same time. I perceived at once that I had encountered the hand of Hines, an intuittion that I relayed to Captain Gomes. "I trust your instincts here, Sergeant," he answered.

I met with Dr. Culpeper in Magnolia to share the story, which hadn't yet made it around the community. "That does sound like Hines," confirmed the doctor. "Why? In God's name, why?" I pleaded. "Well, Sergeant, I'm afraid that ain't even the half of it. That sorta thing I 'spect we'll be seein' a lot more of down here fer years ta come. Now only leave it ta radicals like Hines in an absence of order ta perpetrate somethin' on such a scale an' within y'all's vicinity. He rode with the St. John's Rangers 'fore he paid out for commutation, same as some of them up yonder in the 2nd Cavalry. He has impunity here, ta say nothin' of cooperation. I'd say the Johnnies have essentially turned him loose on you all . . . and always keep in mind that Mrs. Hines was educated in Boston, like a number of these ladies, so don't think your superiors are necessarily ignorant of it all. But this rollin' boil of centuries here is bound ta turn inta steam anyhow, an' the South will be hemorrhaging black bodies alive an' dead fer a long, long time. If anythin', this war has made the slow march of death a great race ta annihilation for our black brethren, fer that war that might make it otherwise is not one anyone on earth has the spleen ta wage. All it takes is one more Jackson, an' the South may well sweep the whole Union inta slavery again." Dr. Culpeper took a cigar into his mouth and realized he'd become lost in his words. "I'm sorry, my boy," he said. "When one scarcely gets ta speak, the stuff just comes right out." I smirked at the older man. "And you," he asked me, "how will you fare after this debacle? For I know how the South will. The big an' the long houses will be gone, but that'll be all. And not one of your comrades will mind a bit. So why must you?"

I shook my head and said, "Doctor, I only know one country, and that's the one in the Book. I'm not here to cast lots for the clothes off the negroes' backs."

"Ah, so you are a fierce Republican, yes? All the better! We'll have the house ta ourselves soon, and with any luck, we won't even be states anymore, just wide open land—"

"—which belongs to the negroes," I interjected.

"Does it, now? I know some will take it, but it all depends on what can be accomplished. Tell me, are these all jubilee years? We know jubilee better 'an yer Puritan forefathers did. At Christmas the slaves come wakin' up the masters, are feasted an' served like they was masters themselves, an' expect gifts. Slave an' master may sit in the same church, but jus' once a year may he take the master's pew. How congenial it is, too, knowin' His law don't abide our lowly conditions. But believe me, states or not, ten percent or fifty percent, and whatever the color or party of the governin', you will *not* remove the planter from this land, and the South shall have its mistress again. The holy door on the Potomac will close, and the reversal of roles will just as quickly end." I stood to take my leave of this man, clearly agitated by his worldview. "Sergeant," he called after me, "the poor will always be with you, you know." I held his pinewood door open and looked at him. "May they remain safe in my keeping," I said, and left.

We drilled ceaselessly in those days. The bugle calls directed our lives, but I suppose it is the good fortune of the cavalry that our horses learn the calls, as well. One morning in camp, the men dismounted for inspection, which we left to our corporals as we higher non-commissioned officers met on the other side of the camp. We were so engaged, speaking on mundane camp matters, when a report issued from out of the woods. In an instant, I witnessed poor Shadrack's head, which had theretofore been casually reclined to one side listening to Sergeant Cook, burst open and release its contents. The commotion set his horse into a fit, and the rest of us fled quickly between the rows of tents. I will never forget that sight. Captain Gomes told us that the sentries had captured the sharpshooter, a young boy from Magnolia, but this only unsettled us more. From then on, we couldn't expect safety anywhere, it seemed. Rumors in the camp circulated that the boy was one of Hines' "Seminoles," and that the act was calculated to increase the general pathos of terror among us. Captain Gomes made little of such rumors, and ordered us to admonish any of our charges promulgating such stories.

Still, if these tales were true, we had then a lot more to worry about, as our gains in Florida also marked the arrival of the direct-tax commissioners. In and around Magnolia, the populace would be obliged to witness wholesale confiscations and the turning over of lands to scalawags and carpetbaggers, while any impromptu show of Confederate patriotism by a child could cost an entire family their home and imprisonment. The heavy Federal plow was felt to sink itself deep into the riverbanks as the tangled mess of roots braced for impact. War is indeed the ultimate Saturnalia, not leastly for its barbarity and licentiousness, but also for the pageantry of its supposedly upending order and fortunes, yet only selectively, and for only a time. I am permitted, surely, to pity those whom Johnson's forgiving arms could not embrace, be they black poor or white poor. I couldn't see any more sense in separating Shadrack from his pears and conferring all his orchards to the Lowells or the Cabots. My comrade could not have died for this.

The day came for our assault on Middleburg. Fifty-five of us rode from Magnolia, expecting to enter Middleburg by surprise owing to Mr. Nowlins' information. This by my estimates was achieved, as we passed the Halsey place quietly, and only met a light skirmish closer to Black Creek. Pushing through that, we crossed over the south prong of the creek and entered the town, setting fire to many of its buildings, including storehouses. The conflagration made the whole country aware of our presence, and in short order, the rebel cavalry were riding our way. On the next day, then, we quit the town, burning the bridge over Black Creek as we left. Still, the graybacks were able to ford that creek farther upstream and rout us near another creek around the Halsey farm. We buried a number of our men in the moss-covered soil of Magnolia Springs after that confrontation, and I myself was thrown from my collapsing horse and into a tree stump, resulting in the shoulder injury that still haunts me. Returning disheveled with our wounds and our dead, the folks of Magnolia stood around in awe at the spectacle. There, amid all of the populace thusly assembled around the assortment of homes composing the place, Captain Gomes announced, "Sergeant Randolph, you may at once convey your gratitude to George Nowlins for these achievements." I was astounded. The Captain rode away, and I surveyed the crowd of locals and soldiers, drinking in the effluvia of river and war from my gaping mouth. One man, a fisher from the waterfront, shook his head. Another group of Magnolia men made themselves to look busy. "Sergeant," someone touched my arm lightly, "the infirmary. Your shoulder." I nodded compliantly, stealing another glance around the assemblage of civilians. Then my eyes chanced upon Corporal Leigh. "Corporal!" I called. His face was splattered with blood, but I could not detect an injury to his person.

"Sergeant Randolph, sir?" he answered.

"Corporal Leigh, I need you to go to Mr. Nowlins' house right away. I will tell you where it is, and what to say to him. This is very important, Corporal. Take a handful of your men if need be. I need you to guard the Nowlinses' house day and night, Corporal, do you understand?"

Leigh contorted his face as he looked at my shoulder. "Sergeant, I—"

"I know, do you think I can't feel the blamed thing? Now come, do as I say!"

As my injury was treated, I refused all drink, aware that Mr. Nowlins' life now lay in my hands. Despite this, I was unable to refuse the land of Nod to which I was hastened by the pain. When I awoke late in the night, my arm was bandaged and immobile. I dressed quickly, however, and took a horse out to the Nowlinses'. Oh, in those times when one rushes into a discovery the mind prepares the way for acceptance of the worst. That was how I arrived to find the Nowlinses' small cottage in disarray, door broken, with Mrs. Nowlins sobbing on the steps, her garments torn and her hair violently shorn. "They—they—they—they—they take 'im, . . ." she stuttered. I couldn't remain with her. "The sentry?" I asked. She looked at me with consternation. I rode off toward Magnolia.

"Leigh!" I called from my horse amid the boarding house, saloon, and residences. A drunk man missing an arm stumbled up to me with his bottom lip curled like a sausage and his one arm on his brow in salute. "You know who that war', Lieutenant?" he asked, misidentifying my rank. He moved closer, stroking my horse and shushing it. "Lieutenant, yer sent'nel absquatulated. . . . 'e war' fuckin' that black bitch, Hines' hussy," he said. Suddenly my midnight ride came to a halt. The man stroked and shushed the horse some more, as it whipped its tail. The river rolled on, and some quiet din of laughter was heard from inside one of the structures. Hines and his "Seminoles" had made it through like a cool draft, and now there was no way to close the window. "Lieutenant," the drunk man continued, "I tol' that music boy in the s'loon 'e better stop pissin' on my shoe. He war' pissin' on my shoe!" His pitch heightened as he raised one foot, teetering as he did so. I left him without a word, returning to camp.

In the dark quiet, I rode past the captain's tent, staring at its surfaces, imagining it breathing with movement. No, I couldn't challenge Gomes like that. I rode to the end of the row and found Cyrus standing, keeping watch. We exchanged nods but remained in silence. He watched the row, and I did so with him for a moment. I wondered to myself. Unbelievable suspicions behind the uncertainty of daylight battles etched behind the midnight eye. "What have you seen?" I whispered from my saddle. The sentry shifted his eyes toward me, keeping his head steady. "Raccoons," he spoke softly, "raccoons. Comin' an' goin', stealin', runnin' back off inta tha hammock. I seen lots a raccoons." He kept his stiff posture, and his eyes rolled back toward their forward-facing position. "War ain't been hard on tha raccoons, nope. I think I seen tha fat ones gettin' fatter." I sniffed and wiped my nose on my sleeve. I could feel the pain in my shoulder returning, and I was growing dizzy. I bade Cyrus goodnight, returned the horse, and slunk back into my quarters.

The next morning, as I sat without eating, watching a fire smolder, a vedette reported that a white man was hanging upside-down from a live oak branch over the mouth of Black Creek with his entrails dangling into the water below, food for turtles and catfish. A straw rope tied around his breast held a strip of bark bearing the inscription, "SCALLYWAG POSSUM." It was Mr. Nowlins. "Did you cut him down?" I asked. The young conscript looked confused. "Well, cut him down!" I yelled angrily at him. He rushed off to comply. My rage simmered inside me. It felt as though we were presently losing the entire war without so much as a plaintive flinch. It wasn't the case on paper, no, but the army as I knew it seemed like no war juggernaut, let alone any moral one. We were still weeks away from Sherman's march to the sea, but I was already hardened against any chorus of "Marching Through Georgia." I was stewing in these thoughts as I waited for Corporal Leigh to make his presence known. Finally he did, returned to camp from whatever godforsaken hole he'd been hidden away in. I suspect he had already been back to the Nowlinses', and found it empty. He dismounted and approached me, straightening his kepi on his head. "I already know," I hollered out over the ashen logs of the campfire before me, with my head in my hand. Leigh swallowed and nervously smiled. "W—What d'you know, Sergeant?" he asked. I pivoted my head back on my neck abruptly and looked at him with a pouting grimace. "B'cause dem wasn't orders," he replied defensively. "Me men . . . me man were 'sposed ta relieve me. . . . Private Barton! Private Rogers!" he feigned aggression at the two, in absentia. He narrowed his gaze and stepped forward, repeating quietly, "Dem wasn't orders, Sergeant. You were convalesced, an'—an'—"

"Corporal, there are stables needing cleaning. Let's look into that before Privates Barton and Rogers show up, yes?"

"Yes . . . yes . . . yes. . . ." Leigh nodded nervously, backing away from the campfire toward his horse. He didn't turn to face his horse and mount it until he'd touched it with his hand, extended searchingly behind him. After he had mounted and trotted a few paces, he faced me with a grin. "Nigger girl was clean as a widow's weddin' dress, Sergeant." I raised my pistol from behind my back, cocked it, and aimed it at him. He hastened his gait and disappeared in the direction of the stables.

I allowed myself to convalesce for some time after that, both for the sake of my shoulder and for that of my mind. I did drink quite a bit, and took only pleasure in that and in periodically emerging from my quarters to make Corporal Leigh's life more miserable. Primarily what I dreaded about recovering and rejoining the war then was seeing Winnie Nowlins somewhere, disgraced and deprived of her husband. Furthermore, I dreaded receiving orders from Captain Gomes, knowing that I distrusted his leadership so much. Dr. Culpeper was called into the camp infirmary once, and he passed my quarters to inquire as to my health. I mostly stared at him, unwilling to speak. He spoke aloud some assortment of things pertaining to the Florida climate and landscape and healthfulness. I disregarded all of it, and before long he tired of trying to engage me in conversation, and he left.

Several weeks had passed, and I was preparing to avail the U.S. Army with my service once more when a crack of gunfire broke through the camp early in the dawn. I leapt out into the officer's row with my carbine and looked toward the source of the noise. There, not twenty paces from me to my right, stood Cyrus with his rifle lowered, still smoking from the shot. Shifting to my left, I saw several men arriving at the place where a small black body in a skirt had collapsed. "Cyrus . . .?" I inquired, agasp. "Hines' hussy!" someone down around the body said. "Cyrus?" The negro sentry looked at me expressionless. "I think I done seen a raccoon, Sergeant. I think I done shot one, comin' outta Captain's quarters." I looked back to my left and saw Captain Gomes emerge from his quarters, red in the face in nothing but his shirt and drawers. I was speechless. Cyrus remained frigid, watching the ensuing commotion. "All's well!" Captain Gomes proclaimed with his hand raised. "Good job, sentry," he added, hobbling back into his quarters. On his way, our eyes made brief contact, but his betrayed nothing. "Funny, she sho' look like a raccoon, Sergeant," said Cyrus. "Cyrus," I told him flatly, "as for the good of the hunt, you know your quarry well enough to shoot at your discretion." His weight shifted to one side. "Woo! That'd be nice," spoke Cyrus. "That'd be powerful nice, Sergeant."

Ultimately the 2nd Florida Cavalry made it to Magnolia a month after our raid on Middleburg. We fended them off, but the tide was turning in the area, and we could sense it. The people of

Magnolia demonstrated a newfound coolness toward us. Or most of us, anyway. In these days, the Captain kept some company with Dr. Culpeper and others in town, and rumors spread that the Captain had purchased land near Magnolia Mills at the suggestion of the doctor to be put to use after the war in profiting from Northern winters (regardless of the victor). As for most of us, our morale steadily decreased. Horses were butchered at night, provisions stolen or urinated in, and all whispers indicated it as the work of the "Seminoles" come from out of the swamps and woods around us. I learned that Corporal Leigh had the clap, and he was treated with silver nitrate. "I heard de doctor gave de captain dis stuff, too," Leigh told me. "I tink dis was on porpose, dis clap de graybacks ha' spread around us."

We wouldn't have to wait long for the end that we were all expecting. One morning, us officers were called to form before the captain, and we all expected what was to come. We all believed that our misadventures on this side of that broad river were about to come to an end, and we all suspected that the 2nd Florida Cavalry would continue on into St. Augustine. We felt that there was something about this river that foretold the defeat from the beginning. The St. John's ominously moved northward to the ocean, to Jacksonville, passing Magnolia, springing from deep within the southern frontier. It flowed from some wretched spring where Florida Water gushed from the Fountain of Youth at the cotton throne of some reptile king, fanning himself with Stephen Foster sheets. It pushed us back north, from whence we came, against a wind that offered to blow us back upstream again if we should ever return with broad enough sails stitched together from our Northern textile mills. "The climate, the climate," said the wind over the ocean, "good for the overworked industrialist."

As we were thusly assembled on horseback awaiting instructions, Captain Gomes stood on foot before us speaking to a civilian. The civilian was tall and maybe a little stout, dressed as though he were prepared for a hunt. In this fashion we were kept waiting for a tiresome span of minutes. At last the captain turned to face us. He cleared his throat. "Gentlemen . . . we will be returning to Jacksonville." There was a palpable sense of relief in the air. "There, we will continue our service with the Department of the South."

"Hines," I heard whispered, as the captain continued speaking. Again, "Hines." I looked back at the civilian to whom Gomes had been speaking. He stood confidently, chest protruding, a crooked smile on his lips. He held a large cigar. 'Could it be?' I thought.

". . . We will be suspending any furlough requests for the time," spoke the captain.

"Hines," said another voice, more audibly. This made the captain and the civilian tilt their heads in its direction. The civilian smiled more broadly. The captain cleared his throat. His speaking did not commence again. He stepped back toward the civilian, sword bouncing against his thighs. The man handed him some papers as they shared some words.

At length, the captain stepped forward toward us again. "All right," he yelled. The officers looked at one another. I thought I could hear the soft, twisted Spanish moss above us swaying in the Autumn air. The captain seemed frightened or embarrassed for an instant, or at a loss for words. We heard the report of a woodpecker high up in some trees hammering its head against the callused trunk of some uncaring Florida tree. The atmosphere made a convincing elixir, and for a moment, the war was as far away as the unforgiving mills of New Bedford. For a moment I was quite near cajoled into floating haplessly on my back below the swaying of the canopies, blissfully heedless of the alligators and moccasins and other assassins all around.

"Jubilo done pass," Hines blurted out, spitting on the ground and then rolling the cigar around in his mouth. "Y'all go on home now."

An artist's depiction of a fight in Volusia County, Florida, not far from Jacksonville, first published in the *Courier-Journal*, January 1865.

The Untold Story of the 2nd North Carolina Mounted Infantry

Patrick Barton

Introduction

Much like the discordant times preceding the American Civil War, the United States is currently going through a significant transition. In the last few years, the uncomfortable truth about the Civil War has truly been exposed, albeit in fits and starts. Within the last decade the onerous Confederate battle flag was removed from the South Carolina capitol building, and, more recently, the historic *Silent Sam* statue was defiled and razed at the University of North Carolina. Confederate statues are coming down, from Stonewall Jackson on Monument Avenue in Richmond, Virginia, to generic soldier statues in Jacksonville, Florida, amidst armed protests; and the Mississippi legislature voted to remove the Stars and Bars emblem from their state flag. Similar to the tumultuous period of the 1860s, America has again become divided. Divided about issues stemming from a war that concluded over 155 years ago.

The unfortunate part of the acrimony that comes with turbulent times is the polarization that occurs. In the south, many people cling to legacies of ancestors who played a part in the Civil War and assume the unenviable task of protecting their memories. Unfortunately, this often inappropriately motivates southerners to preserve false ideals of the Confederacy, perpetuated and promoted for years by politicians, educators, and even academics. Of all the Civil War myths clinging to life, the most damaging is that of the unified south. This fable perpetuates the incorrect belief that all southerners unfailingly supported the Confederacy and were willing to fight to the death for the cause. Even more problematic is the fictitious certainty that slavery had little or nothing to do with the war, thereby consolidating slaveowners and non-slaveowners toward a common cause.

Among the memories whitewashed, or indeed, completely destroyed, are the accounts of the southern men who did not subscribe to the Confederate propaganda. These were the men who struggled to maintain Union alliances in the heart of the Confederacy. Historian John Inscoe cleverly referred to these disremembered ancestors and the events surrounding their alleged treason toward the south as having "Unionists in the attic," a perfect description if ever one existed[8]. These men and their activities not only shatter the façade of the unified south, but they also shed light on the time and the volatility of emotions during the period. Indeed, these men and their actions are the true legacy of the Civil War in Western North Carolina and East Tennessee. They represent the untidy truth of the Civil War.

These men also demonstrate further evolution of the fighting in Appalachia by transitioning from a ragtag band of "renegades" to a legitimate combat unit in the Union Army's order of battle[15]. The following investigation delves into the storied history of the 2nd North Carolina Mounted Infantry, formed in the hinterland of the Confederacy. Further, this examination outlines the points of contention and attempts to explain the dichotomy that existed in the coves and hollows of Appalachia. To that end, slavery, secession, economics, Appalachian culture, and politics will all be scrutinized as parts of an overall structure that tore the fledgling nation apart.

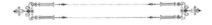

Seeds of Discontent

In order to grasp fully the motivations behind the men of the 2nd North Carolina Mounted Infantry, the events leading up to the secession crisis must be understood in two contexts: one being the national scale involving all states and peoples, and the second being the context of a poor, Appalachian, yeoman farmer with limited education. Both of these lenses are equally important in the study of the Civil War in Appalachia, and they are inexorably intertwined: one aiding understanding of the other and providing a necessarily broad view. The first of these issues, and indeed, the spark that ignited the powder keg of sectional politics, is that of slavery.

A commonly held belief in modern Appalachia is that slavery played little or no part in the motivations of ancestors to align with the Confederacy or with the Union. Lieutenant Colonel William W. Stringfield of Thomas' Legion mused, "A great majority of the people were poor and had not interest in slavery[2]. . . ." This assertion, however, doesn't pass the litmus test of logic. The fact of the matter is that slavery did exist in Western North Carolina, and the presence of slavery impacted the economy, the people, the land, and other factors. And while slavery didn't have a significant presence in Western North Carolina, prompting historian and author William Freehling to label this section of the south as a "white belt," denoting a majority of whites[6], the impact was inescapable.

Freehling's assertion and the logic behind it are further buttressed by the census of 1860, which provides unique insight into the racial makeup of Appalachia and allows for reasonable assumptions on the impact of slavery. By far the largest population of enslaved African Americans was centered in Burke County, North Carolina, which had an enormous 27 percent of the population working against their will, compared with 2 percent in Watauga County, North Carolina[2]. These incredible spreads follow the terrain of the land, with Burke County being among the flattest in the Piedmont, and Watauga being among the most mountainous. Western North Carolina averaged 10.2 percent across the listed counties. This constitutes a significant minority by any measure, and the economy invariably will be shaped by a labor force that consists of a substantial minority of enslaved persons.

The most dramatic feature of the numbers of enslaved people is what could not be captured by the census takers in 1860—it serves as measure for the distribution of wealth in Western North Carolina. Historian Eric Foner noted that by 1860, the amount of the net worth of all enslaved people in the south amounted to more than was invested in railroads, banks, and factories in the U.S.

combined[5]. Enslaved workers were expensive, and thus, a "luxury" reserved for the wealthy. Those same wealthy individuals also farmed the best land, at a profit, in contrast to the average poor yeoman farmer of Western North Carolina, who struggled to feed his family, to which Stringfield alluded.

Despite the vast amount of money invested in slavery, the average southerner did not possess enslaved laborers. Therefore, the average southerner did not believe that he had a vested interest in the "peculiar institution," nor did he share commonalities with elite slaveowners[5]. This fact was borne out in voting numbers demonstrated during the vote for a referendum to investigate secession in early 1861[6]. The vote verified in dynamic fashion that the citizens of North Carolina, particularly those of the western parts, had no intention of allying with their southern neighbors who had already seceded. Indeed, even Governor Zebulon Vance, a slaveowner and Western North Carolina native, had been a keynote speaker at the Union convention in 1860[18].

Another example of the sharp difference of opinion and explosive consequences of the secession/slavery issue was aptly demonstrated in Madison County, North Carolina, during the 1860 vote on holding a secession conference. It was during this vote that a man named Nealy (sometimes spelled Neely) Tweed, a staunch Unionist, became physically confrontational with County Sheriff Ransom Merrill, a professed Confederate, in a violent exchange of political ideas that left Tweed's son wounded and Merrill dead[18]. The Tweeds and Merrills occupied the same county, had similar ethnic backgrounds, had largely been raised with similar values, yet they disagreed so much over the direction of their state that tensions erupted into a conflagration of gunfire and murder.

An interesting example of the societal stratification that was evident in the antebellum south can be found in the words of its vice president, Alexander Stephens. He stated, ". . . [The Confederacy] is the first government ever instituted upon the principles in strict conformity to nature, and the ordination of Providence, in furnishing the materials of human society[13]." Further on in the speech, Stephens attempts to clarify that all white men were equal in the eyes of the law[13]. His meaning in the message is found in the subtext. Kings, lords, and other rulers in the European tradition have often justified their own success by claiming it was granted by a higher power. This was referred to as divine providence, or the divine right of kings to rule. The Confederacy was founded upon slavery supported by God's blessing. This mantra left those unable to afford enslaved workers being consigned to the lowest caste, barely "above" the enslaved laborer himself[13].

It was this unspoken rule that forever separated the southern aristocracy from the plebian farmers. The divine origins of the structure served to justify many evils in the minds and deeds of the wealthy. By celestial declaration, the wealthy, a superior species, deserved the greatest tracts of land, education, money, and political dominion over the yeoman serfs. This very idea negates the prospect of upward mobility of poor southern men. This would upset the delicate balance of power dictated by God. These factors, simmering injustices borne from the British Isles, erupted into a cataclysmic display of violence that left one young man injured and a law enforcement official dead. These same points of contention would spark the deadliest conflict in American history at that time. Importantly, it is similar perceptions of injustice that spark the continued debate of the Civil War and its legacy today.

Tensions Erupt

The outbreak of war quickly followed the hostile events of late 1860. Despite the secession of several states—including North Carolina's southern neighbor, South Carolina—the North Carolinians had declined even to seriously consider secession, albeit by a narrow margin[6]. Events developed at Fort Sumter, however, off the coast of Charleston, South Carolina, violently shoved the nation over the brink. It was this misunderstood incident, compounded by effective propaganda, that sealed the fate of nearly 650,000 men.

The Fort Sumter crisis was truly a display of inappropriate machismo by the newly formed Confederate Army and an unfortunate dilemma for President Abraham Lincoln. When Lincoln sent in an unarmed supply ship to restock the dwindling supplies of the fortress, the Confederates believed they had no choice but to unleash cannonade after cannonade at the isolated fortification[6]. The Confederate's lack of choices was entirely a product of their own making and a direct result of the inflammatory and boastful rhetoric spouted by its leaders, such as Stephens. Despite these now well-known and thoroughly documented facts, the siege and attack of Fort Sumter played perfectly into the Confederates' agenda.

In states such as North Carolina and Virginia, who were still teetering on the precipice of indecision, the Fort Sumter incident was the tipping point. Lincoln immediately called for 75,000 federal troops from all states in order to forcefully put down the rebellion that had now escalated to violent clashes[6]. To many in North Carolina, this was the first step in an invasion by the north, who'd march through their state to get to South Carolina. This was the worst of all fears perpetuated by the wily secession commissioners and other rabble-rousing politicians. As a result, North Carolina screamed for secession by passing a completely unanimous resolution in the wake of the Fort Sumter incident[6]. Even the resolute Governor Vance was swept up in a wave of Confederate zeal and accepted commission as a colonel in the Confederate Army[18]. Vance would not be the last Unionist to abandon federalist leanings in favor of rebellion. However, many men in Western North Carolina still felt no affinity toward their Confederate overlords.

It was not long after the split of North Carolina from the Union that another military unit was formed. This unit was optimistically designated as Thomas' Legion, and holds the distinction of being North Carolina's only "legion" in the Civil War—although numerically nowhere near a legion[2]. Officially it was identified as the 69th North Carolina Regiment in the Confederacy's order of battle. The organizer of the legion and its namesake was William "Little Will" Thomas, a man of great local renown. Thomas was a personal friend of John C. Calhoun, the infamous early secessionist and war hawk, but Thomas' most unique asset was his connection with the Cherokee Indians[2]. Thomas was a gifted politician, and this was aptly demonstrated in his dealings with the remnants of the

Cherokee during the Civil War.

Although white, Thomas was a member of the Cherokee tribe and a great proponent of their interests. Thomas' master stroke, however, was undoubtedly his success at recruiting the Cherokee into the Confederate Army under his command[2]. This was even more incredible for the fact that the nascent Confederate government had made no real attempts to recognize the rights or grievances of the Cherokee, and the ideals espoused by President Jefferson Davis and his vice president obviously conflicted directly with the inclusion of the Cherokee[13]. Despite the popularity of Thomas' early coup with the Cherokee, many soldiers would soon become disillusioned with the Confederacy and take an opposing stance.

George W. Kirk, a young man from Greenville in East Tennessee, who had been a staunch supporter of the Union, similarly abandoned Unionist sentiments in the aftermath of the perceived northern aggression. Kirk enlisted in the Confederate volunteers following the secession of his state. He quickly became disillusioned by the Confederate cause, however, and he deserted the army[12]. Kirk, like many Appalachians, was not the type to accept subservience to false prophets like the leaders of the Confederacy. In the tradition of his Scots-Irish/English ancestors, Kirk maintained a fierce sense of independence. It was this spirit, and perhaps a powerful moral compass, that guided Kirk to join the Union Army, quickly gaining a commission as an officer[12]. The decision to join the federals initiated Kirk's meteoric rise to stardom during the Civil War.

Kirk did not serve in the Union as a regular soldier. He was not, at least initially, involved in classic set-piece engagements for which the Civil War is famous. Kirk became a scout and a guide for the Union in the mountains of East Tennessee and Western North Carolina. He soon graduated to recruiting, training, and leading Unionist bushwhackers (guerrilla partisan fighters) from his mountainous stomping grounds[12]. Many of these initial recruits were deserters such as he or men who were actively avoiding conscription, while others were simply unsuited to conventional military service but still possessed necessary skills to fight an unconventional war[12].

110

In the mountains of Western North Carolina, finding Unionists was not a difficult task, although it could be a dangerous endeavor, with tempers explosive on both sides. Kirk and his men engaged in raids under the dubious moniker of "bushwhackers" for a couple of years with great success.

Birth of the 2nd North Carolina Mounted Infantry

It was in 1863 that Kirk's fortune changed for the better. By this time, Kirk had solidified his reputation as a fierce and effective partisan fighter and leader. He had fruitfully recruited enough men to rival a unit of military regulars[12]. Despite the damage and considerable fear and confusion Kirk and his men had visited upon Confederate supporters, an important element was noticeably absent from Kirk's already-impressive résumé. That was no official recognition by Union military leaders or legitimacy of command marked by rank and unit designations. However, Kirk was soon promoted to colonel, and the men under his command were designated as the 2nd North Carolina Mounted Infantry and the 3rd North Carolina Mounted Infantry, respectively[12]. With his promotion and acknowledgment, the now Colonel Kirk had both a professional title and the distinction of having been added to the Union Army's order of battle in the southeast.

Kirk's command had been designated as "mounted infantry," signifying that his unit was on horseback[4]. This was a significant distinction between Kirk's unit and other units operating in the area, such as the Home Guard, Thomas' Legion, and the Confederate regulars. Kirk's unit had superior mobility to any other force on the battlefield of the mountains. This capability would enable Kirk to continue the hit-and-run tactics that had met with his success as a bushwhacker. Indeed, the mountainous terrain of Western North Carolina was more conducive to the fast-paced war of maneuver made possible by mounted infantry units than it was to the archaic massed formations employed by units such as the 62nd North Carolina Infantry.

The men under Kirk's command were among the best the Appalachian region had to offer. Many of them had deep roots in the area dating back to the time around the American Revolution, a time when their Scots-Irish/English pioneer ancestors strove to carve out a life in the rugged backcountry of the Blue Ridge and Smoky Mountains. The vast majority of these men were drawn from Buncombe and Henderson counties in North Carolina, with smaller contingents coming from all corners of Western North Carolina and East Tennessee, as well as from other southern states[1]. Men such as Corporal Francis Blackwell, Private Jeremiah Taylor, and Corporal Robert Justice, all soldiers of Company H of the 2nd North Carolina Mounted Infantry, had heritages in the area dating to the 1740s. They still have descendants thriving in Henderson County, even one who has authored Civil War articles involving the rich local history of the area[1]. It was a unique cross-section of men that all decided to take up arms in defense of the Union in the face of overwhelming local Confederate opposition.

The enlistment records of the 2nd Mounted Infantry paint an interesting picture of the unit and concurrently serve to define the unit as the epitome of southern independence. The men under Kirk's command were commonly labeled as "Tories" by the Confederate soldiers and sympathizers of their hometowns, an allusion to the different loyalties that existed during the American Revolution[2]. The disparaging label was meant to draw a comparison to the sympathizers of King George during the Revolution, thereby branding the men of the 2nd Mounted Infantry as traitors lacking patriotism. Ironically, the men of the 2nd were rebelling against an autocracy that bore more resemblance to rule under the British crown or medieval feudalism than did the government of Lincoln. However, the view of these men as traitors to the cause, or anti-southern, persisted long after the war and continues to prevent accurate depictions of the war in Appalachia[8]. Despite this, Kirk and his men, and others like them, would play a crucial role in the ultimate triumph of the Union over the Confederacy[6]. Answering the call of destiny, Kirk and his men set about preparing for a long war, locked in the heart of the Confederacy.

Not one to rest on his laurels, Kirk quickly set to work searching for duties and actively seeking out engagements. The 2nd Mounted Infantry was assigned to the Union Army command based in Ohio, but they were stationed in Greenville, Tennessee, until mid-October of 1863[6]. It was fortunate that Kirk and his men had been engaged in combat before becoming legitimate combatants in the Union Army because the 2nd was soon to have its mettle tested in the fires of combat. Their first recorded action of the Civil War was at Walker's Ford around Clinch River in Tennessee. They joined with elements of the 14th Illinois Cavalry, the 2nd Regiment of Tennessee Infantry, and others for the engagement[11]. This amalgamation of forces fought to secure Union gains and flanks in the aftermath of the successful Chattanooga Campaign. Although Walker's Ford was a miniscule rendezvous in Civil War history—indeed, it was merely a small skirmish—it proved the men of the 2nd were capable of holding their own in combat[4]. Although the 2nd Mounted Infantry was not destined to win the field at Appomattox Courthouse or even to participate in a major battle, the men would leave their indelible mark on towns and villages of Western North Carolina.

Scorched Earth: Stoneman's Raid

By 1864, the 2nd Mounted Infantry had undergone some significant changes. The unit had grown to the point that it was split. The men of the 2nd Regiment had been joined by the new unit of 3rd Regiment. Furthermore, their valiant leader, Col. Kirk, had been reassigned to command the newly formed 3rd. The men of the 2nd were placed under the tutelage of the New York native Lieutenant Colonel William C. Bartlett[3]. By this time, the overall command and charge of the unit had changed from the Ohio command to the Cumberland command under the venerable Brigadier General Davis Tillison and his soon-to-be-infamous superior Major General George Stoneman[3]. Despite these changes and rapid expansion, the men of the 2nd Mounted Infantry had been relegated mainly to scouting and patrol duties. These were duties that were well suited to the highly mobile unit but were not conducive to being active participants in major engagements.

Despite the lack of combat, save for a few skirmishes with bushwhackers and detachments of Thomas' Legion, the 2nd Mounted Infantry was still active in the Union order of battle, and their moment of glory was fast approaching. The leader of the new campaign, General Stoneman, had started the war in an inauspicious fashion. He had attempted to match the successes of such Confederate raiders as Nathan Bedford Forrest and John Hunt Morgan; in these endeavors, Stoneman had failed miserably and had even been captured[7]. With a new command and renewed vigor, however, Stoneman resolved to punish the Confederacy. He famously quipped, "I owe the Southern Confederacy a debt I am anxious to liquidate[7]. . . ." Fortunately for Stoneman, by this time in the conflict, the remnants of the Confederate Army in North Carolina were mere shadows of what could be mustered in 1861-2. Stoneman, on the other hand, had an ever-growing batch of disenfranchised southern soldiers who, like Stoneman, had a score to settle with the oppressive Confederate regime and their local sycophants.

Stoneman and his highly mobile force of cavalry and mounted infantrymen crossed into North Carolina from Tennessee on March 28th, 1865. Upon his entrance into North Carolina, Stoneman and his men engaged in a conquest of terror, setting the Boone jail ablaze and utterly annihilating a drained and inept Confederate Home Guard unit[7]. Due to the predictable direction of the attack, local Confederates had forewarning of the impending doom. One area in particular that was at risk was the Morganton area in Burke County, which had the largest enslaved population of all the western counties[2]. While the enslaved population was not in itself problematic for the men of Stoneman's unit and the 2nd North Carolina Mounted Infantry, it was the embodiment of the haughty southern planter elite that was enraging. Not only did these barons have the most property and liquid assets to lose, but they drew the ire of the "home Yankees" and, therefore, were marked for retribution[9].

These fears would prove to be well founded. In the raid on Boone, an elderly man named Jacob Councill was diligently working his field along with his enslaved laborer when Stoneman's men arrived. Upon interrogation, Councill attempted to declare neutrality in the conflict, but his enslaved worker contradicted this statement and revealed the true Confederate leanings of his "master." Councill was summarily executed by Stoneman's men with a hail of rifle fire[9]. Stoneman then set his sights on the Piedmont area near Morganton and Lenoir. The policy of scorched earth and retribution followed with Stoneman's men as a factory was next torched[7].

In what can only be described as a comprehensive rout, Stoneman and the 2nd charged headlong through the Piedmont area and then worked their way west. The unit finally reached the home turf of many of the soldiers of the 2nd—Henderson County—on April 22nd[3]. Even the citizenry of Henderson County, however, was not to be spared the carnage and thievery. A significant drawback of having a force of cavalry/mounted soldiers was that horses became exhausted, sick, or even killed by overexertion or battle. By extension, this necessitates the acquisition of new horses for the continuation of the spearhead. In this manner, many citizens would suffer —including those who truly were innocent, unlike Mr. Councill.

In Henderson County lived the first female physician in North Carolina's history, Dr. Polly King Justice. She was illiterate but learned medicine as her husband read her medical books by the firelight. As was common for physicians of the time, Dr. Justice relied heavily upon her trusty steed to spirit her to needy patients. However, her horse was taken by Stoneman's men during the brief occupation. The seizure of the horse was reportedly made while a gun was held to the head of Dr. Justice's husband, the local justice of the peace[10]. Actions like these would contribute to the postwar image of the men of the 2nd North Carolina Mounted Infantry and other "home Yankees," who would be reviled by their southern brethren for generations to come. To bear arms against one's brother was unconscionable in the traditional southern mind.

Stoneman and the men of the 2nd continued their drive west, but an interesting turn of events would delay the advance. During their historic penetration into the Confederate hinterland, Union General William Tecumseh Sherman had soundly defeated Confederate General Johnston, and General Lee had surrendered at

Appomattox Courthouse to General Grant. Based on these decisive defeats, the local Confederate commander, Brigadier General James Martin, had agreed to a surrender under the terms established between Sherman and Johnston[7]. In nearly all the land east of the Mississippi, the Civil War had come to an inglorious end for the Confederates, while leaving the Union the undisputed rulers of the land. The politicians in the U.S. government, however, rejected the terms agreed upon by the Sherman/Johnston pact, and in an instant the war was back on[7]. Instead of maintaining current positions and awaiting the men in charge to broker a more palatable cessation to hostilities, Stoneman took it upon himself to put the Union in a better position. It should be noted that at this time, the Confederate Army had been soundly defeated and routed on all fronts. Thus, the logic behind Stoneman's aggressive decision is certainly suspect, especially considering his own storied history with the Confederate forces.

Despite the obvious defeat of all significant Confederate forces, Stoneman ordered his subordinate, Brigadier General Alvan Gillem, to "bring Johnston to better terms" by initiating a raid on the unofficial capital of Western North Carolina, Asheville[7]. It was the subsequent actions of the men, including those of the 2nd, that would further add to the notoriety of the Union men as a whole, and add fuel to the already raging inferno of familial hatred in Western North Carolina. Gillem and his men raided Asheville and committed crimes of pillaging and plundering on a monumental scale[7]. No residence or citizen was safe from the villainy of the Union men. Author Chris Hartley noted the words of a resident as ". . . pillage of every character, and destruction of the most wanton[7]." The atrocities committed in the sack of Asheville were legendary and personified the worst in humanity. In a historical twist of irony, John Inscoe and Gordon McKinney noted that most residents in Asheville were initially pleased with the entrance of federal troops because it signaled the end of a protracted conflict and also liberated the besieged and closeted Union sympathizers stoically holding out in the city[9]. The sudden reversal of policy regarding plunder and misconduct by the Union troops continues to be a subject of historical speculation.

116

After the barbarous treatment of the Asheville residents, the men of the 2nd had reached the end of their war. For the mounted infantry, this marked the end of a prolonged struggle marred by losses of men and equipment along with assignment to secondary duties in the defense of their beloved Union. For the next few months 2nd and 3rd Regiments were charged with mundane occupation duties before finally being released from service when the unit was deactivated on August 16th, 1865[4]. The men were now free to return to their homes, carrying with them the successes, triumphs, defeats, and atrocities they were either complicit in or had carried out. Against all the odds, these Union guerrillas, Confederate deserters, outlaws, and dedicated Unionists had not only forged a successful unit in the midst of the now-defunct Confederacy, but they had fought bravely, reflecting their humble upbringings and commitment to a cause of freedom and independence.

Aftershocks and Remembrance

The men of 2nd North Carolina Mounted Infantry were not held in high regard by their fellow citizens. For some, it was not difficult to see why. However, this was the story of the Civil War in Appalachia: a war of brother against brother fought with hitherto unknown brutality. Of course, this was compounded by the incessant propaganda machinations of the Confederacy. Perhaps the best example of this is found in the unabashedly Confederacy-sympathetic newspaper called *The Western Democrat*. In spite of the fact that Kirk was a mountain boy himself, the newspaper spared him from no disparaging remark. One contributor to *The Western Democrat* labeled Col. Kirk and his men as a "diabolical outrage" and further compared Kirk to an "Irishman's flea," which was a derogatory allusion to a colloquial parable representing Kirk's failure to engage in a conventional battle[14]. Kirk's mention, however, even in such a demeaning manner, assisted him in gaining the attention of the Confederate forces and the public at large.

Despite Kirk's growing popularity by the readers of *The Western Democrat*, the editors were careful to mention Kirk as an after-thought. In fact, he was at some points referenced as the archnemesis of the significantly more popular Thomas' Legion[16]. This archetypal conflict between a hero and a villain captured the imagination of the readers. In this narrative, though, Kirk was often not even given credit as a Union officer in command of a legitimate fighting force. Instead, he was referred to as leading a band of "bushwhackers," "outlaws," or even renegade criminals[16]. These references were made to Kirk and his men right up until the latest stages of the war in 1865. This method of classifying Kirk and the 2nd was only marginally effective, as evidenced by the influx of men into Kirk's charge throughout the breadth of the conflict.

However, the Confederate-leaning newspaper did effectively manage to encapsulate and express the utter hatred that Confederates had for Unionists. Again, this was highly reflective of the emotional and political turmoil of the period. It is not difficult to see why, when the engagements of the 2nd are viewed through the evanescent kaleidoscope of small-town politics. In one example, the men of the 2nd engaged the regulars of either the 62nd North Carolina or 64th North Carolina Infantry on or about March 24th, 1865. The engagement occurred in the notorious area of Shelton Laurel in Madison County, site of the horrific massacre. In this engagement, the men of the 2nd, many of whom were from Henderson County, killed one of the Confederate regulars named Henry Gilbert, who was also a resident of Henderson County[14]. It is difficult to imagine the pain of the Gilbert family, knowing that their loved one was slain by his own neighbors, indeed potentially a member of his own family. This type of close-quarter and personal killing often engenders significant emotional repercussions and serves only to polarize the parties further.

Unfortunately, the men of the 2nd Mounted Infantry did not cease their plunders after the unit had disbanded. In one of the final editions of *The Western Democrat*, the defeated yet unrepentant editors highlighted the continued misdeeds of "Kirk's command [of] deserters and other lawless men[17]." The newspaper demonstrated no restraint in describing the nature of the "daily violent outrages

. . . and frequent murders" that were occurring in Henderson County and elsewhere[17]. Even months after the deadly conclusion to the Civil War, the Southern Democrats and Confederate sympathizers were still angry enough to pen impassioned diatribes against the victors. However, the suspiciously widespread nature of the incidents and the distinctly undetailed description of the atrocities calls their validity into question, though it does speak to a larger point involving the "traitors" of the 2nd North Carolina Mounted Infantry, and indeed, the Civil War itself.

The unfortunate fact remains that many southern and Appalachian Americans still view the Civil War, and its participants and agitators, through the skewed lens of that belonging to a revisionist or apologist. This view, much like that of *The Western Democrat*, not only obscures the truth but attempts to minimize or even erase the contributions of men like Colonel Kirk and the men of 2nd and 3rd Regiments, while simultaneously erecting statues, both literal and philosophical, in remembrance of men like "Silent Sam" or General Robert E. Lee. Lee, himself, believed that the Civil War should not be remembered in that manner, and commanded this unambiguously in personal correspondence with friends. These delusions, like the diminished contribution of the 2nd Mounted Infantry, are reflective of a broken system still infested with revisionists. However, the final lesson of the 2nd is never to give up; continue the fight even in the face of overwhelming odds and powerful propaganda. Victory is always close at hand.

Colonel George Kirk, c. 1870.

Cherokee Confederates of Thomas' Legion at a reunion in New Orleans, 1903.

A corresponding numbered bibliography can be found in the back of the book.

Georgetown Girls

Eneida P. Alcalde

Georgetown: Tuesday, October 22, 1861.

Nine-year-old Abbie sat with her bare feet over the edge of the bed, clutching her ragdoll in her arms. She stroked the doll's long skirt, the cotton fabric soft on her fingers, and stared at Liam sleeping on his bed across the room. Illuminated by the moonlight filtering through the window, her four-year-old brother looked like an angel tucked under the quilt—except there was nothing angelic about his snoring. Abbie listened to his wheezes and watched his mouth open and close. He was a deep sleeper no matter the circumstances, even when Daddy was away in Washington City.

The window rattled from a gust. Abbie shivered, feeling the cool night air. She placed her feet back on the mattress and pulled the quilt and sheets over her body. Lowering her head onto the pillow, she lay on her side and covered her ear with her doll. She closed her eyes, but she could still hear Liam's snores. She opened her eyes and yawned, stretching her arms.

A loud creak from downstairs froze her mid-stretch. Another creak resonated, softer than the first, followed by a thud. Abbie took a sharp breath, recognizing the front door opening and closing. She sat up and pressed her ear to the wall by her bed. She heard the faint sound of footsteps coming from downstairs. Her chest tightened. Daddy was away—only supposed to return at dawn from his shift at the hospital.

Not wanting to disturb Mommy, who was in the next room with baby Jack, Abbie slowly rolled over to the other side of the bed. If baby Jack awoke, he'd cry—and who knows how the intruder would react. Besides, Abbie was the oldest—the only sibling who could go downstairs without Mommy's or Daddy's help. She clenched her fists, determined to find out who had entered their home in the middle of the night.

Abbie set her feet on the wooden floor and placed her ragdoll on the pillow. Miss Emma had made the doll for her last birthday. At this late hour, Miss Emma and her daughter Betty, the family's house slaves, would both be sleeping downstairs. Abbie shuddered, worried the intruder might harm them.

She tiptoed to the door by the foot of her bed and gently twisted the knob and pulled. Abbie stuck her head into the hallway. To her right, she saw darkness where her parents' bedroom was located. To her left, moonlight seeped through the sheer curtains of the window at the end of the hall. She stepped into the hallway and tiptoed toward the window. Once she reached it, she peered down the stairwell. A flickering yellow light illuminated the bottom steps. The intruder must have lit the candle by the foyer. She listened for more footsteps. Not hearing any, she clutched onto the oak handrail and descended, stepping quietly onto each narrow step.

When she reached the first floor, she saw the lit candlestick on the maple stand by the front entrance. Next to it lay her father's iron house key. Abbie breathed easy and grinned. She turned left and entered the corridor. A dim light radiated at the end of the dark passageway from the kitchen at the back of the house. Eager to surprise Daddy, she rushed to the light. Her right hand traced the corridor's papered wall as she passed the parlor and the dining room on her left. A few feet from the kitchen, she felt the familiar warmth of the fireplace on her cold feet.

Abbie entered and froze in place. At the other end of the room, her father sat at the slaves' dining table with his back to her. He was hunched over with his elbows resting on the tabletop and his head buried in his hands. Miss Emma stood across from him between the fireplace and the stew stove watching a pewter teakettle steaming on the iron stovetop. Miss Emma's eleven-year-old daughter, Betty, slept on the straw bed the two shared. Curled on her side, Betty clutched the ragdoll Miss Emma had made for her. It was identical to Abbie's doll.

Abbie stepped past the bed, moving to the middle of the room. "Daddy?" she said in a whisper, not wanting to wake Betty.

Miss Emma looked at her. Her eyes widened, and she shook her head no.

Abbie ignored her concern and took a few more steps toward her father. "Daddy? What are you doing back home?"

Daddy raised his head. "Abbie, sweetheart, please head back to bed. It's awfully late for a girl to be up." His voice was soft but strained.

The kettle whistled. Miss Emma lifted the pot off the stove and walked to Daddy. She tipped it over a large tin pan in front of him, filling the pan with hot water.

Abbie walked up behind her father. Miss Emma dipped a cloth into the hot water and wrung it before wiping down Daddy's hand. When she dipped the cloth back into the pan, a dark liquid mixed with the water. Abbie tapped her father's shoulder. He turned and grabbed her wrist. Shocked by the tightness of his grip, Abbie yanked her hand away. She scrunched her eyebrows together and glared at him.

He closed his eyes and exhaled, then opened his eyes, staring at her. His blue eyes were gray in the firelight. "I'm sorry. It has been a very difficult night, and I am in an ill mood." He touched the side of her face with his wet hand, running his thumb over her cheek. "Forgive me."

Abbie looked down at her feet and back at him. "Of course, Daddy."

"Sir, your other hand, please."

He gave Miss Emma his other hand, and she wiped it down.

Abbie sat on the chair next to Daddy. From this angle next to him, she could see dark blots covering the front of his shirt. "What are those?" she asked.

He frowned and set his hand on the table. "I'm afraid it's some poor fellow's blood."

Abbie folded her hands on her lap. "Sorry, Daddy."

"You have nothing to apologize for. I simply dislike being so frank with you about such horrid matters. But it's unavoidable under the hellish circumstances." He pressed his lips together. "More wounded arrived tonight. We saved as many as we could."

Abbie placed her hand over her father's hand like she had seen her mother do many times since the war started. She remembered one of the Bible verses Mommy liked to repeat: "For he maketh sore, and bindeth up: he woundeth, and his hands make whole." Abbie smiled. Her father placed his hand over hers.

Miss Emma brought the wet cloth to his face. "Your eyes, sir."

He closed his eyes. The hard lines around the corners of his mouth softened as Miss Emma wiped his face and mustache.

"Your shirt, sir."

He opened his eyes and unbuttoned his shirt, revealing the birthmark in the middle of his chest. It reminded Abbie of a flying bird. Slipping his arms out of the long sleeves, he took it off and set it on the floor. "There's no point in salvaging this one. Might as well burn it."

"Yes, sir."

Miss Emma set the wet cloth on his chest and wiped the dried blood off him. Daddy kept his eyes closed. She dipped the cloth back into the water pan and wiped again. After Miss Emma removed all the blood, she picked up the soiled shirt off the floor and placed it in the pan with the dirty water. She lifted the pan, set it against her hip, and headed to the back door. Miss Emma opened it and walked outside to the backyard. As the door closed, Abbie felt the autumn chill enter the room. She covered her hands with the frilly cuffs of her nightgown sleeves.

Daddy observed Abbie with a calm expression. "I am headed back to the Washington Infirmary after I check on your mother. A carriage will return for me within the hour."

Abbie nodded, remembering Mommy's aches the day before from her pregnancy. She had lost a baby years ago before Liam was born.

"I don't know at what time I'll return. Hopefully, by late morning."

Abbie groaned. "You'll miss breakfast."

He leaned in close to her and pushed one side of her auburn curls behind her ear, away from her forehead. "There was a battle in Leesburg. More wounded are coming. They will need my attention."

"Is Leesburg far away?"

"Far away in Virginia. You will sleep safe and sound." He placed his hand on her arm. "I must tend to the men fighting on behalf of the Union. Do you understand?"

"I do."

Miss Emma stepped back into the kitchen carrying the empty pan. She walked past them to the pantry near the bed she shared with Betty, who continued to sleep.

Daddy squeezed Abbie's arm. "It's past midnight. Tomorrow is a school day, Miss Abigail Anne McGill."

Abbie giggled at hearing her full name.

He stood up. "Let's leave, so Miss Emma can rest. It's been a long night for her, too."

Behind Daddy, Miss Emma spun around to face them. She clasped her hands together. "It's no trouble, sir. You are doing the Lord's work attending to them soldiers."

Daddy glanced back at her. "Thank you, Miss Emma. We all try our best." He held out his hand for Abbie. She grabbed it, and he pulled her up from the chair. He bent his knees low and patted his back. "Ready for a piggyback ride?"

"Yes!" Abbie jumped onto his back and wrapped her arms around his neck.

He hoisted her up by her legs and held her tight before straightening and heading to the corridor. Abbie laid her head on his shoulder, comforted by his familiar warmth.

"Oh, sir," Miss Emma said as they exited the kitchen.

Daddy paused in the darkness of the corridor. "Yes?"

"I'll leave a clean shirt for you by the door."

"Thank you, Miss Emma. I don't know what we would do without you."

"Goodnight, sir."

"Goodnight, Miss Emma."

Daddy resumed walking down the corridor. When he walked by the foyer, he blew out the candle. As he climbed the stairs, Abbie felt her body grow heavy. She fought to keep her eyes open. The world looked different from Daddy's tall point of view, even in the dark, and she wanted to see it. Entering the upstairs hallway, Abbie yawned.

"Abbie," Daddy said and opened her bedroom door. "I'm going to kneel so you can hop onto your bed."

"Yes, Daddy." Abbie placed her feet on the mattress. She sat, grabbed her ragdoll, and spread out. She watched Daddy's silhouette pull the quilt and sheets over her, tucking her in. Behind him, Liam slept on his tummy, no longer snoring.

He kissed her on the forehead. "Goodnight, my princess."

"Goodnight, my daddy."

The last sound she heard before falling asleep were his footsteps headed to the room next door to check on Mommy.

Later in the day, after Abbie arrived home from school, she wandered into the kitchen, hoping to find Betty. Betty sat on a stool scrubbing the inside of a pot. Next to her, Miss Emma stood over the sink washing dishes. Abbie leaned against the wall by the kitchen entrance and clicked her tongue. Both Betty and Miss Emma looked at her.

"Well, hello, young lady," Miss Emma said. "You hungry? That school of yours not feeding you proper?"

Abbie smiled. "Not hungry. I came for Betty."

Miss Emma arched her eyebrow. "And who's gonna help me clean up? These dishes ain't gonna get up and wash themselves."

Betty rolled her eyes at her mother.

"I need Betty's help to wake Daddy up," Abbie said. "I promise it'll only be for a little while."

Miss Emma placed the dish she held in the sink. "Is that so? Your daddy's such a bear you can't get him up yourself?"

Abbie's lips trembled from suppressing a laugh. "I was also hoping she could read *Uncle Tom's Cabin* with me. Just a chapter or two."

Miss Emma smiled. "I see. Well, if you're gonna be doing something educational, I suppose Betty can go."

Betty jumped up and slipped off her apron, revealing the light-gray cotton work dress she wore. It was a size too big for her thin frame and frumpy in comparison to the royal-blue school dress

Abbie had on. Betty set the apron on the stool and approached Abbie. Her hazel eyes gleamed.

Miss Emma shook her head. "You best not be gone all day. You hear?"

Betty glanced at her mother. "I won't."

Abbie grabbed Betty's hand, smaller than hers. She led her down the corridor. Both girls giggled as they skipped. The wide skirts of their calf-length dresses bounced with each step. Passing the parlor, Abbie heard her mother call out her name. She tugged on Betty. They stopped by the room's doorway. Mommy sat on the sofa holding baby Jack who slept on her lap, wrapped in a wool blanket. He sucked on his thumb and curled against Mommy's protruding stomach where another baby grew. Liam sat on the rug in front of them, playing with his blocks, stacking one on top of the other. Behind him, logs burned and crackled in the brick hearth, releasing warmth.

Mommy stared at Abbie. "Don't create a ruckus."

"We're going to wake up Daddy and read *Uncle Tom's Cabin*."

Mommy forced a smile. "If he's not in the mood to wake up, leave him be. He came back late this morning given all the fighting in Leesburg yesterday."

"Yes, Mommy."

Her mother placed her hand on the leather-covered Bible lying by her on the sofa. "*Uncle Tom's Cabin* . . . haven't you read that abolitionist puffery at least ten times? You should be reading the Bible. Our soldiers could use your prayers."

Abbie pressed her lips to hold back a groan. "Maybe we can do both."

Mommy tapped the Bible. "Take it with you."

Abbie walked across the room and picked up the Bible.

Mommy grabbed her arm and pulled her close. She whispered into her ear, "Remember the words of the Lord: it is more blessed to give than to receive. Pray for God's mercy. Pray for our soldiers."

Abbie felt her mother's hot breath on her skin. "I will, Mommy."

Mommy stared past her to Betty in the hall. She spoke in a raised voice: "Betty should pray, too. That'll help her understand the sacrifices we're making for her kind." Mommy released her grip. Up close, Abbie noticed dark circles under her eyes and a few white strands in her long, red hair.

Abbie headed back to Betty, feeling the weight of the Bible in her arms. The girls continued down the hall without exchanging a word. They passed the front entrance and turned right toward the stairs.

"So, we're not gonna read *Uncle Tom?*" Betty asked.

Abbie stopped near the stairwell and looked at Betty. "Oh, we'll read *Uncle Tom.* We just need to memorize a verse or two of this Bible so when Mommy asks about it, we can repeat the verses."

"Mm. She won't know better?"

"Trust me, she won't know. She'll soon fall asleep for a nap."

Betty set her hand on the Bible, feeling the leather cover. "This one's much prettier than the one me and Mama got. . . ." She took her hand off the Bible. "Your ma's been so quiet to me and Mama these days. Is everything all right?"

Abbie lowered her voice. "I think it's because there's a baby on the way. Makes her restless. She also worries about the war."

"Can't blame her. War's awful scary. And the fighting's so near us."

Abbie narrowed her eyes. "Daddy says it's far away."

"It ain't."

"How do you know?"

Betty crossed her lanky arms behind her back. "Mama talks to the sellers on Herring Hill. They know all sorts of stuff. I overheard when we was there this morning."

Abbie tilted her head. "Maybe I can go with you one of these days."

Betty's eyebrows shot up. "Don't you think it'll be odd?"

"Well, I can sneak out with you on Saturday morning."

"That's not what I meant." Betty pointed at Abbie's red hair. "You'll stick out. Not sure Mama will want all that attention. Hard enough with every other negro man asking her out or asking about me."

Abbie frowned. "Why do they ask about you?"

Betty's lips curled into a half smile. "Why do you suppose?"

Abbie's cheeks grew hot. "I don't know."

"My skin don't match Mama's." Betty smirked. "You don't see that my skin's lighter?"

"Didn't think much of it."

Betty rolled her eyes. "I figured."

"Well, I still want to go to Herring Hill."

"Your folks'll never let you. It's a negro neighborhood."

"Daddy will let me."

"Maybe," Betty said with a chuckle.

Abbie hugged the Bible to her chest. "We should head up before Daddy wakes." She started up the stairs, and Betty followed behind her.

Even in the daytime, the stairwell was dark, lit only by the early afternoon light streaming in from the upstairs window. In the dimness, Abbie climbed the stairs holding onto the handrail. She wondered how the negro sellers got their war information. Maybe they read the newspapers. She sighed. Mama always burned the war articles in the hearth before Abbie could read them, claiming she was *too young* to read about the war. It was the same reason she gave for not letting her go with Daddy to Lincoln's inauguration. Reaching the second floor, Abbie promised herself to find out as much as she could from the sellers, if she managed to sneak out with Betty and Miss Emma on Saturday.

Abbie picked up her pace, passing the closed door to her bedroom. She heard Betty's soft steps behind her. Soon the girls stood outside her parents' room. Abbie bent over and set the Bible on the floor, leaning it against the hallway wall.

Betty tapped her shoulder and pointed to the Bible. "Ain't that disrespectful?"

"Don't know. It's too heavy to bring inside. We'll get it after we wake him." Abbie unlaced her black-leather boots and took them off, setting them next to the Bible.

Mimicking her, Betty took off her work slippers and placed them on the other side of the book.

Abbie grasped the doorknob and opened the door. The sunlight flowed in through the middle slit of the thick curtains, lighting the bedroom just enough for her to see Daddy sprawled out on the bed.

He slept on his stomach with one arm hanging over the bedside. She brought her forefinger to her lips and glanced at Betty. Betty grinned.

The girls tiptoed toward Daddy on the other side of the room, passing baby Jack's crib on their way. Once they were close to Daddy, Abbie stuck her pinkie into her mouth to wet it. Betty covered her own mouth with her hands. Her body shook in a silent fit. Abbie bit her tongue to suppress her own laughter and leaned closer to her father's face. He slept with his mouth open—a bit of saliva hanging from the side of his lips. Abbie brought her wet pinkie to his ear. She held her breath and inserted the pinkie into his earhole, smearing saliva inside. Daddy's eyes flew open. Abbie pulled her pinkie out. Betty laughed out loud.

Daddy blinked his eyes and looked at Abbie then at Betty. He lunged forward, first grabbing Abbie by the waist and then Betty by the arm. He hauled both girls onto the bed, one on each side of him with his long arms around them, tickling their tummies and sides. "You rascals!"

Abbie writhed and kicked, squealing to get away, but Daddy's tickles kept her in place. Tears streamed from her eyes as she heard Betty laughing and howling along with her. Abbie closed her eyes, releasing another fit of hoots and giggles.

As fast as he had started, Daddy stopped. Abbie caught her breath and overheard Betty doing the same. Her father nudged her with his arm, and Abbie opened her eyes. The room was bright— the curtains wide open. Mommy stood there, holding baby Jack on her shoulder. Liam stood next to her.

Mommy's eyes shifted from Abbie to Daddy to Betty as they sat up on the bed. "The master's bed is no place for a house slave."

Abbie looked at Betty, who lowered her head. "But Mommy, she—"

Mommy stomped her foot. "Hold your tongue. I saw you left the Bible on the floor."

Abbie grabbed Daddy's hand. He squeezed it.

Mommy glared at Betty. "Are you going to sit there all day?"

Betty got up from the bed with her head down.

Mommy took a few steps forward stroking baby Jack's back.

Liam walked with her, holding onto her floor-length skirt. They stood in front of Abbie and Daddy. Mommy glowered. "John, I'm tired of all the abolitionist nonsense you feed her."

Daddy lifted his chin to face her. "What do you mean?"

"You know what I mean. All she does is read that *Uncle Tom* book when she should be reading the Bible. God knows our boys need all our prayers." Mommy side-eyed Betty. "And I don't know of any other proper girl who plays with her slave—on the master's bed of all places! I'm going to need these sheets washed."

Daddy released a long breath. "Do you hear yourself? Are those God's words spouting from your mouth?"

Mommy huffed. "It's one thing for you to be an extremist. It's another thing for you to indoctrinate my daughter."

"*Our* daughter, Ellen."

Abbie leaned against her father's side. "Daddy doesn't force me."

"A slap is what you deserve for your insolence and unladylike behavior. You're lucky your brothers are with me." Mommy scowled at Betty who now stood closer to the door. "And Betty, you'll go without supper for the rest of the week. Then you'll remember that you are just an ordinary house n—"

"Enough!" Daddy slapped his leg.

Betty ran out of the room, her quick steps fading down the hallway.

Liam whimpered into Mommy's skirt. Mommy stroked the back of his head but kept her eyes on Daddy. "You and your ideals. You ever ask yourself what it costs the rest of us?" Mommy's voice cracked. "So many of our boys dying . . . for what?"

"Abbie," Daddy said, "take your brothers downstairs." He pushed on her back.

Abbie scrambled out of the bed. She stood in front of Mommy, avoiding her stare. Mommy passed Jack to her. Abbie held him with both arms and placed him upright against her shoulder. He yawned and continued to sleep. Liam clutched Abbie's skirt and sniffled. Abbie wobbled to the door, taking slow steps, feeling her brothers' weight on her. She heard Daddy get off the bed and approach. When she stepped into the hall with Jack and Liam, Daddy stood behind her in the doorway.

"I'll close the door," he said.

"Thanks, Daddy," Abbie said in a whisper without looking back at him.

The door clicked shut. The Bible lay against the wall where she left it, between her boots and Betty's slippers. With baby Jack in her arms, she pushed her feet into her shoes, balancing herself against the wall. She resumed walking, the loose laces of her boots dragging on the floor. Liam followed her. Passing their bedroom, Abbie thought of her copy of *Uncle Tom's Cabin* lying on the bookcase by her bed. She wished she had another set of hands to grab it.

When she reached the stairs, Abbie leaned against the wall to catch her breath. Almost a year old, baby Jack weighed about twenty pounds, making for a hefty load. After a few seconds, she overheard Mommy shouting. Not wanting for Liam or Jack to hear the argument, she went on, glancing over her shoulder every other step to check on Liam. He clutched her skirt from behind and grabbed the balusters to steady himself. Halfway down, they locked eyes.

"What's wrong with Daddy and Mommy?" he asked.

"Daddy's an abolitionist, and Mommy doesn't like it."

"What's an *abolonit*?"

Abbie smiled at his mispronunciation and stepped onto another stair. "People who want slaves to be free."

After a few more steps, they made it to the first floor. Abbie led her brothers into the parlor. Baby Jack half-opened his eyes and gurgled. She placed him on the sofa and stroked his forehead. He closed his eyes, falling back asleep. Liam sat on the rug by his blocks. He picked up two, setting them on top of each other to form the base of a new stack.

Abbie sat next to Jack, resting her hand on his warm tummy. She leaned back into the sofa, hearing her parents' voices through the ceiling as they argued. She shut her eyes, longing for a nap. But then she heard hurried steps against the wood flooring, approaching her. She opened her eyes. Miss Emma and Betty approached. Betty's face appeared puffy as if she had been crying. She walked barefoot, having left her slippers upstairs.

They stopped in front of Abbie.

Miss Emma stood behind Betty, a full head taller. She placed her hands on Betty's small shoulders and regarded Abbie, her eyes still and unblinking. "Betty told me what happened."

Abbie sat up straight, placing her hands on her lap. "I am so sorry, Miss Emma."

"No point in apologizing. Just nice flowery words." Miss Emma opened her mouth to continue, but closed it. She observed Liam who continued playing with his blocks. She focused her attention back to Abbie. "I do feel for you, Miss Abbie. But the world is not built on apologies. You have to see things from where I'm standing."

Abbie's neck tensed. She offered a slight nod. Betty stared past her at the street-facing window, her lips pursed.

Wetness lined Miss Emma's dark eyes. "This here's my whole world. I got to do all I can to protect her." She wrapped her arms around Betty's shoulders. "I don't want you coming around asking her to play with you. No more of that."

Betty tugged on Miss Emma's sleeve. "Mama . . ."

"No, you gonna have to trust me. I know it hurts, but it's for our own good."

Abbie wiped her wet cheeks with the back of her hand.

"Don't take it personal." Miss Emma's voice quivered. "Got nothing against you. Matter of fact, I do have love for you. Just not as much as my own. I have to protect what's mine."

Betty lowered her head as Miss Emma looped her arm through her daughter's, holding her close. Miss Emma led her back to the hall.

Once they were out of sight, Abbie watched Liam knocking down the stacks he had built. He paid no attention to her, engrossed in his own world. She looked at Jack still asleep, his tummy rising and falling with each breath. She admired his blond curls and touched his hair. It was soft and lush. Her lips trembled. Her brothers were too young to be her playmates. She didn't care for blocks or sleeping for long periods of the day. Betty was her best friend—had been her best friend. And now they could never play again because of Mommy.

Abbie covered her wet eyes with her hands. Footsteps marched down the stairs. Daddy soon appeared in the entryway. Through her fingers, she glimpsed him entering the room. Liam pushed himself up from the floor and ran to him. Daddy scooped Liam into his arms.

"Do you ever stop playing with your blocks?"

Liam giggled.

Daddy kissed him on the cheek and approached Abbie. "Thanks for taking care of your brothers."

Abbie kept her hands over her eyes, not wanting him to see she had been crying.

Daddy set Liam on the floor. "Can you build me a fort?"

"Yes!" Liam plopped down on the rug and rearranged his blocks.

Daddy squatted on his knees in front of Abbie and tightened the loose laces of her boots, tying each up. He took her hands, removing them from her face, one by one, and ran his thumb under her eyes, wiping her tears. "Do you want to talk?"

She averted her eyes to her lap. He stroked her red curls, leaned close, and kissed the top of her head. Abbie wrapped her arms around his neck and released a whimper.

He embraced her. "One day, you'll have the opportunity to change things, so we take better care of one another."

She pressed her cheek onto his shoulder. "I hope so, Daddy."

He stroked her back. "You will."

Baby Jack released a piercing cry, kicking his little arms and legs. Daddy let go of Abbie and lifted baby Jack off the sofa. His cries lessened as Daddy cradled him, rocking him back and forth.

"He must be starving. I'm going to take him up to your mother."

Liam glanced up from his blocks. "What about my fort, Daddy?"

"I'll come back to see it." Daddy smiled at Abbie. "Besides, your sister's here."

Liam pouted and placed a block next to another.

Daddy walked away with baby Jack. He entered the hall and looked back at Abbie.

Abbie smiled at him and scooted off the sofa to the rug. She sat on her knees by Liam to watch him finish constructing his fort. Daddy's footsteps faded in the background.

Abbie felt someone shaking her arm. She opened her eyes. Her father's outline stood before her in the dark, leaning close. He placed a finger on her lips and grasped her hand, pulling her off the bed, into his arms. She held onto him with her arms around his neck, holding her ragdoll in her hands, with her legs around his waist. Nearing the door, Abbie heard Liam releasing soft snores. Daddy opened the door, stepped into the hallway, and closed the door softly.

"What's the matter, Daddy?" Abbie asked.

"Shh. We'll talk when we're downstairs."

Abbie set her chin on his shoulder, comforted by his familiar scent, a mix of shaving soap and tobacco. She wondered what this night adventure was all about as he carried her through the hall. He stepped onto the stairs, which released a loud creak. Abbie felt Daddy's chest expand under her grip. He exhaled and held onto the oak handrail. He took another step—this one slower than the first. The stairs did not creak. Taking slow steps, he continued down.

When they reached the bottom floor, the foyer was completely dark. Daddy touched the walls to find his way. Upon entering the corridor, Abbie lifted her head. A dim light emanated from the kitchen. Once inside the kitchen, Daddy set her on the floor. She twirled around—her long nightgown spinning with her. Miss Emma and Betty stood together in the middle of the room, wearing their long, black coats and boots. A brass candlestick flickered on the kitchen table. Not a single flame came from the fireplace. Betty held her ragdoll. Miss Emma held a shawl.

Abbie grabbed Daddy's hand. "Hi, Miss Emma, Betty." She lifted her heels off the ground. "Are you visiting Herring Hill? Am I to go with you?"

Miss Emma stepped forward. "No, child. We have a different

trip to make."

Abbie scrunched her nose and looked up at her father. She squeezed his hand. "Daddy?"

He glanced at her and tapped her nose with his finger. "Tonight, I handed Miss Emma and Betty their freedom papers."

Abbie's mouth opened. She looked at Miss Emma and then at Betty. "But I love them."

Daddy placed his arm over her shoulders. "That is precisely why we must let them go."

Abbie noticed the square, leather suitcase by Miss Emma's feet. Abbie ran her hand over her ragdoll's yarn-curls and whispered, "I wish, Papa, they were all free."

Daddy rubbed Abbie's arm. "Papa? Who's that?"

"Eva's father. Eva says this to him in *Uncle Tom's Cabin*."

Betty lifted her eyes. "Any mind that is capable of real sorrow is capable of good," she said in a trembling voice.

Abbie recognized the quote from the book. She met Betty's gaze and walked to her, pressing the doll to her chest. "Don't you know that Jesus loves all alike? He is just as willing to love you, as me. He loves you just as I do, only more. . . ." Her voice faltered, unable to complete her favorite quote, seeing Betty's misty eyes. Abbie took in a deep breath and held Betty's hand. It felt warm in her grasp.

They stood observing each other.

"Girls," Daddy said. "Miss Emma and Betty must leave. The carriage waits outside."

Abbie's breaths quickened. She felt her father's firm grip on her arm, tugging at her. She released Betty's hand.

Daddy took the shawl from Miss Emma and wrapped it around Abbie's shoulders. He picked up the suitcase by the handle and grabbed the candlestick from the kitchen table. Daddy then guided Abbie to the corridor, following Miss Emma and Betty, who walked ahead. As they left the kitchen, Abbie stared at the bed Miss Emma and Betty had shared since Betty was born, two years before Abbie's birth. The bed was made, as if no one had ever slept on it, with the sheets and old, gray quilt folded in under the straw mattress.

Halfway down the corridor, Daddy blew out the candle. Abbie's eyes adjusted to the dark, enough so she could detect the others' outlines as they walked. They stood in place once they arrived at the foyer. Daddy stepped away from Abbie, moving ahead of Miss Emma and Betty to the foyer's interior door. The door clicked as he opened it. Moonlight filtered in. Daddy placed the candlestick on the maple stand and picked up the iron house key before heading to the front door. Abbie heard the familiar click of the door unlocking. Daddy handed Miss Emma the suitcase, and she stepped outside with Betty. Daddy then came back to Abbie, lifting her in his arms.

Walking past the small dogwood tree in their front yard, Abbie spotted a carriage on the cobblestone street. The driver sat in the front seat holding onto the reins of a horse whose breath was visible in the cold air. The horse's black-brown coat gleamed under the full moon. Abbie noticed the row of two-story brick homes across the street, their windows dark as Daddy approached the carriage. The dogwood leaves rustled from the light wind.

Daddy waved at the driver. The driver tipped his top hat. In the dim light, Abbie could see the man's smile through his bushy, gray beard and thick eyebrows.

"I'll let you inside with Betty, so you can properly say goodbye."

Abbie kissed her father's cheek. "Thank you."

Daddy unlatched the carriage's side door and pulled it open. He set her inside. Surprised by the softness of the carriage floor on her bare feet, Abbie looked down—she stood on carpet. She inspected the square interior, which could easily fit four passengers. Abbie sat on the elegant plush seats, covered in burgundy satin. She pulled the wool shawl tighter, soft against her skin, and rested her doll on her lap.

Daddy lifted Betty by the waist into the carriage and closed the door. Betty sat on the seat across from Abbie, holding her own doll in her arms. Despite the doll, Betty seemed different in her black coat and boots—she appeared older.

"Where will you be going?" Abbie asked.

"Mama says we first go to Philadelphia. See how it is." Betty touched her doll's yarn-mouth smile with her finger.

"Philadelphia. So far away."

"Mama says it's a two- or three-day trip."

Abbie wrapped one of her doll's yarn-curls around her finger. "How will you get there?"

"Carriage, mostly. Mama said something about stopping at some house on the way."

"You think it's safe?"

Betty shrugged and stared out of the carriage. "Should be. Your daddy gave us those papers and arranged the trip himself."

Abbie followed her gaze. She saw Daddy talking with Miss Emma by the dogwood tree. She leaned closer to the window and squinted her eyes, trying to see better through the night. A hand on her knee made her turn around.

Betty knelt in front of her. Her hazel eyes appeared gray in the moonlight. She placed her doll on Abbie's lap next to Abbie's rag-doll. "She should stay with you."

"Oh, she shouldn't." Abbie handed the doll to Betty.

Betty pushed the doll back on Abbie's lap. "She should stay with you."

Abbie placed her hand over Betty's. "But your Mama made it for you."

Betty smiled. "Mama can make another. Simply ain't fair to separate them. These dolls are sisters."

Abbie studied the dolls—their matching yarn smiles and button eyes. She swallowed and looked at Betty. Her stomach knotted up. "Don't leave."

Betty's smile disappeared. "We have to."

Abbie's eyes blurred. The dolls lay side-by-side on her lap. Her tears fell on their cotton dresses, seeping into the fabric. She felt Betty's hands on her shoulders and looked up. Tears clung to the corners of Betty's eyes. Abbie leaned forward and embraced Betty, crying into her shoulder. Betty hugged her, stroking Abbie's back with her hand.

A soft knock on the door, and then it opened. Daddy and Miss Emma stood on the other side. Abbie kissed Betty on the cheek before the girls separated. With both dolls tucked in her arms, Abbie shuffled toward Daddy. Betty sat in her seat and wiped her wet eyes with the sleeves of her coat. Daddy lifted Abbie out by the waist, setting her against his chest. Clutching the dolls in her hands, she wrapped her arms around her father's neck and stared back at Betty. She tried to force a smile, but stopped, unable to control her trembling lips. Abbie buried her face into her father's shoulder. She felt Daddy lean into the carriage to hug Betty with his other arm, and heard him whisper into her ear.

Abbie felt someone rub her back. "This shall pass, child," she heard Miss Emma say.

Abbie peeked out from her father's shoulder to see Miss Emma enter the carriage and sit across from Betty. Daddy lifted the suitcase from the ground with his free hand and slid it inside. Abbie pressed her face against his shoulder to stifle her sobs. She heard the door shut.

The driver snapped the reins. The horse snorted. Its hooves clacked against the cobblestone. The large carriage wheels clattered. Abbie lifted her head. Miss Emma and Betty waved goodbye through the side window. At the end of the street, the carriage turned left, disappearing from view.

Daddy walked back to the house, holding Abbie with both arms.

She bit her lower lip to stop it from trembling. "Mommy will be angry."

Daddy's neck clenched under her grip. "She will."

He entered the home and locked the door. Nearing the stairs, Abbie felt an emptiness inside the house, knowing Miss Emma and Betty were gone.

"Daddy," she said in a low whisper. "Don't let me sleep alone."

He kissed her cheek. "I'll sleep with you tonight."

Abbie held on tighter to the dolls as he climbed the stairs.

Outside of her bedroom, Daddy slid off his slippers and left them in the hall. He opened the bedroom door and set Abbie on the floor. She tiptoed to her bed. Daddy tiptoed behind her. He lay down first, on his side, near the wall. She lay next to him, the dolls in her arms. He pulled the sheets and quilt over them. Abbie snuggled against him, comforted by his presence, even though he took up most of the bed. Liam snored across the room.

After a few minutes, her father whispered, "Does he always snore like this?"

"Every night." Abbie flipped around and placed her ragdoll on his head. "I cover my ear with the doll. It helps a little."

Daddy held the doll over his ear. "Thank you, my princess."

"Goodnight, my daddy."

Abbie cuddled into her father with Betty's doll in her arms. After a few minutes, she heard her father's steady breath. She blinked, and warm tears escaped, following the curve of her cheeks. Tasting the salty wetness on her lips, she kissed Betty's doll and closed her eyes.

The Battle of Ball's Bluff was a Union failure that took place near Leesburg, Virginia, on October 21, 1861. It was an accidental battle, wherein a Union scouting party mistook pointed trees for unguarded Confederate tents in the dark, and while marching toward the "tents" at daybreak, the Union troops instead encountered an unexpected company of Mississippi infantry. When U.S. Senator/Colonel Edward Baker was killed (above, in an 1865 print), the Union troops crumbled and were forced back over the edge of the bluff and into the Potomac River by the Confederates. Many drowned, and hundreds surrendered rather than fall into the water (below, in a newspaper illustration from November 23, 1861).

Death of Colonel Baker
(Song from the Civil War)

William Sutherland

(all sic)
Killed in Battle near Leesburg, Virginia, October 21st, 1861.
Composed by William Sutherland during the Civil War.
Respectfully dedicated (by Sutherland) to Dr. John F. Kaufman.
Air.—"California Brothers"

Our starry flag is at half mast, and the muffled drum beats low,
It tells a sad, sad story, a story full of grief and woe—
Of the death of a soldier hero, cut down in the prime of life,
While fighting for our Country's union, amid the battle's strife.

Brave men are falling, every day; they seem dying by the score,
Ellsworth and Lyons are both dead, and now Baker is no more:
Noble, loyal, true-hearted man! he never felt afraid;
The dashing, brave commander of the California Brigade.

Six balls had pierced his noble breast, aimed by some hostile hands
Who had joined the southern traitors, and entered the rebel bands:
While pushing a cannon forward to his adopted country's aid,
He fell upon the battle-field, while leading his brave brigade.

The gallant Colonel Baker's dead, and a nation mourns for him,
And another murder is added unto the traitors' sin;
At Leesburg, in Virginia, after the close of day,
Brave Baker fell with a mortal wound, while leading on the fray.

He seemed to foresee his doom before the fatal hour had come,
Yet, like a soldier brave, he died, that never the dangers shun,—
Peace to his ashes, let him rest, his name shall forever shine,
And his deeds be read on history's page until the end of time.

Yes, Baker's dead; his battles o'er, he fell, like a soldier brave,
Fighting in the struggle our country's banner for to save,—
Bury him beneath the sod, raise a monument to his name,
And let the nation ring throughout with Colonel Baker's fame.

How many brave men've been killed since secession raised her head!
How many homes left desolate, and how much blood's been shed!
We love our Union, 'tis true, and suffer much to save our flag—
God grant our army victory! may their courage never lag.

U.S. Senator and Colonel Edward Dickinson Baker, c. 1861.

Dr. Mary Edwards Walker Counts the Union Dead

Barbara Alvarado

T he chapel's windows darken
a starlit sky. No moon will glow
through tonight to shine
on the faces of those waiting for dawn's rise.
The quiet lays her low. She wanders
among the rows of cots, their sheets draped
over the sharpness of rusting blood.
The sighs of men blow black the candles
in the room, the whole space heaving
with pain. The nurses' skirts
billow, slow and steady. Like the pendulum
clock mounted on the wall, they swing
the time away, marking ends, marking days.
Her letter rides in her trouser pocket,
ready for the morning post. It expects
another reply to keep her here,
close to beds where no God watches.
The night shift moves on about her.
Her hopes whisper as the smoke of burning pine
melting in the hearth. She stares into its embers,
counting them one by one.

Mary Edwards Walker, shown here c. mid-
1860s to 1890s, wearing the Medal of
Honor that was later revoked due to her not
being a commissioned officer. She was the
first woman surgeon in the U.S. Army and
the only woman ever to win the medal.

The Explosion at the Arsenal

Jamie Todd Hamilton

Friday, June 17, 1864
10 minutes to noon

We are not allowed to talk
It is too distracting
We have to be precise
50 grains exactly
50 grains only
No more no less
50 grains

We sit together on long wooden benches
24
If one gets up
We all need to move
24

Just before noon

It is hot
Especially hot for layers of skirts
We are required to wear

Layers of clothes
Skirts, underskirts
Shirts, undershirts
Daughters of
Women's work
In long sleeves and stockings

My family's only income is
This woman's work

No talking

In the heat, June 17th
Concentrate

Be precise 50 grains
Of gunpowder
Each and every cartridge
50 grains
In the heat for the war
On the benches 24
Counting 50 grains

No one moves unless
We all move

The superintendent laid out flares
In the heat, Mr. Brown?
In the heat of June, Mr. Brown?

I've been doing it for months

It's so hot, Mr. Brown

No talking be precise
50 grains no more
No less

In the hot, in the layers, in the close
Close spaces

It's almost noon
Hoop skirts and undershirts

Very nearly noon

The soldiers need explosives
10 minutes to noon

The explosion shakes us
All of us together
24
The flares, Mr. Brown
The flares are exploding

35 feet away
Sparks fly into
The choking room
Two dozen working

In the gunpowder room
Must be precise
50 grains
Union soldiers need
Explosives
50 grains for the Union

The roof leaves the building
Lungs are burning
Skin is burning
Skirts are burning
Life
A fire ball burning

We cannot move
We cannot run

We cannot climb over the burning
Blinded
We claw and scratch over the dead
24 burning
We die burning

20 die burning in
Women's work
The tin roof was lifted from the walls
Trapped by social circumstances
Trapped in women's work

An investigation finds
Supervisor Brown
At fault no charges filed

No compensation

A collection was taken to bury
The dead

President Lincoln led the funeral procession
Attended graveside ceremonies
20 teenaged girls, most of them Irish
1 supervisor

I cannot run away

On the year anniversary of the
Washington Arsenal explosion, a
memorial monument was erected by
the community to honor the 21
women who died in the tragedy,
photographed here in Congressional
Cemetery, c. 1913.

The young women, ammunition workers filling cartridges with gunpowder, pose in front of the door to their workroom at the Washington Arsenal (D.C.) at some point before the explosion, c. 1863-1864.

The Washington Arsenal destruction and debris after pellets from fireworks came in through the window and ignited the gunpowder on June 17, 1864. Twenty-one people died, almost all of them young women and girls. Note the large tree on the righthand side of both pictures for perspective.

Salzburg, Austria, 1773

Amanda Hodes

Maria Anna "Nannerl" Mozart.

C upboards fade orange from the sun,
   which spills across roofs
of Salzburg daily. Smells of brandy

and schweinshaxe linger like wet
varnish in air, this skin-stuck
heat with limbs of rising dough.

Everything knows its place here:
the canisters and pewter pot,
the dust that drapes the mantel.

Yet I wait for Wolfgang and Father
to return, spinning tales of Caucasus,
Spanish waves, and mahogany sand.

After all, what can't be learned
secondhand? The way Wolfgang
perched by the harpsichord, hawk-eyed

and porous, or the way I cracked
open Bach's spine of Toccata and Fugue.
Secondhand, how I stand here now

as Getreidegasse empties with dusk,
and the sounds of creaking carriages
roll in through the distance.

Maria Anna
Mozart, c. 1785.

*Nannerl Mozart was Wolfgang Amadeus Mozart's older sister. She was a virtuosic pianist who
toured across Europe and was admired by her younger brother. However, her father barred her from
touring once she reached a marriageable age and instead chose to foster her brother's musical talent.
She is known to have written many compositions, but no scores of them remain.*

Cardinal Virtues

Gretchen Rockwell

U nicorns seem sweet and docile, pale
bodies held still, flower-crowned heads lowered

in some lady's lap, but let's be real: there's a reason
they had to be calmed. No one talks about the unicorn

blood-maddened, gnashing teeth whiter than its coat, ichor
thick, splashed with gore and gleaming horn trailing entrails as it rears

and releases a terrible roar. Let's not make any mistakes here. Instead,
let's imagine its keeper: pure of heart and body, sitting below a split-

bark tree with ashy leaves, the serpent of knowledge coiled around
her left wrist, right hand outstretched as the maddened horse

approaches, flanks heaving, sweat and blood spattering its sides.
Imagine: heart pounding, right hand rising as she sits pretending

calm, breath shaky in her chest, to touch that long jaw, see the lips
curl back over teeth before they relax to brush her fingertips. See:

that bellows-belly slow and the knees bend, the white bulk lowering
to nest along her legs, lean limbs bent awkwardly, the rearranging.

She reaches for the snowdrops scattered around their bodies, twisting
their stems one-handed as she strokes the bristled neck. The contradiction

of horseflesh and blossom as she drops the finished crown delicately
over the slick horn and thinks about what her life would be otherwise:

beer-brewing, backache-bending over a churn, babies sucking life
from her body, more mouths every year, like her mother. (Her mother,

who gave her the basket of flowers the day after the miller's son stood
blocking her path to the barn door, flushed, hands twisting in his homespun,

hips forward, feet planted like the grain in her father's field; gave her flowers and silently turned her chin to the forest.) The unicorn found her eventually—

its white sides slick with viscera—and she learned how to subtract experience from knowledge, to read the sum of violence and beauty conjoined, to keep

from losing anything she already possessed. At least, one hopes.
It's hard to tell from the tapestries, to read the intent of bodies laid together

and presented as an allegory to virtue. The unicorns look as pure as the maidens they eternally lie with: fair, lovely, bright. As if they were easy to tame.

These pieces depict Giulia Farnese, the mistress of Pope Alexander VI, with a unicorn, which was a popular sexual reference and symbol of captivity in European and Scandinavian art. Left: *The Virgin and Unicorn*, fresco by Domenichino, c. 1602. Below: *The Lady and the Unicorn*, painting on wood by Luca Longhi, late 16th century.

Above: *The Unicorn Surrenders to a Maiden*, part of the *Unicorn Tapestries*, wool warp with wool, silk, silver, and gilt wefts, South Netherlandish, c. 1495-1505.
Left: *The Lady and the Unicorn: Sight*, part of the *Tapestry Cycle*, Flemish, in the style of mille-fleurs, woven c. 1484 to 1500.

Hopes

Caitlin Mariah

Victoria Berezin imagined her daughter's wedding while getting ready that morning. She saw her little Susie's face melt into a chiseled beauty, the soft lace that would blur her cheekbones as she stepped down the aisle. Susie's blue eyes would be the brightest speck in the entire church, only complemented by the simple silhouette of her grandmother's gown. Victoria knew that Susie would have her pick of fine gentlemen. Victoria could only hope that her own husband, Andrel, wouldn't scare too many of them away. For that matter, she hoped that Junior wouldn't, either.

Although a full year younger than Susie, Andrel, Jr., made sure to shuffle in front of his big sister when they went anywhere. Along the Brighton boardwalk, he would lead the family with an experienced navigator's confidence, even when Andrel would call up from the back where to turn, "Поверните направо, мой солдат," *Turn right, my soldier.* Junior would salute back as confirmation that he heard his father, but his pudgy fingers would swing down in front of his face rather than clearing his eyeline as his grandfather, Boris, had taught him.

"Прямой сын, ты должен держать это прямо," *Straight, son, you must keep it straight,* Boris would yell, demonstrating to Vlad as the elders walked with linked arms. Vlad, becoming nothing more than a confused mirror as the years had passed, copied Boris.

"Do you remember, Vlad?" Boris would start, trying to cram their shared memories back into his head. Boris would fold all of the times they had spent curled in corners of the ship from Russia forty years earlier like a note with the password to his past, as though mentioning the nights they spent practicing English were enough to bring his friend back. Vlad wouldn't remember, but it was his listening that gave Boris hope. Boris, Victoria's father, was the last to have hope. Vlad would keep saluting until they reached home.

Victoria set a pot of water to boil that morning, remembering the many chicken kievs and beef stroganoffs Irina, her childhood friend, and she had made. And all of the golubtsy they'd tinkered with. Boris and Andrel adored golubtsy, always requesting the cabbage rolls in different ways, trying to find the perfect recipe that reminded them of home. As they sat down for dinner, Andrel would say, "На вкус как дома," *Tastes like home*, and Boris would disagree. Two first generations bickering over where they'd had the best golubtsy and what it had inside. Irina never heard any of it, for she made sure the entire table was happy before settling in to help Vlad, her father. Vlad could still use utensils by himself, but Irina wanted to watch, make sure he was eating before she started. The kids would just unroll the cabbage leaves while listening to their father and grandfather talk about their time in the homeland. So, every Tuesday, when the housework was done and the youngest was napping, Victoria would wash and chop the potatoes and onions until Irina came home from work. As a teacher at the community's local schoolhouse, Irina would cart Victoria's three older children back and forth from school.

As young girls, Victoria's mother and Irina's would teach them a new recipe every Sunday after church. They started by learning the spices, which ones to add and how much in each dish. Then they moved on to the chopping and eventually to the meats. After each lesson, they were charged with writing the recipes down, "На английском," *In English*, they would say. To ensure the culture never died but that it worked its way into the American Dream. That's how Victoria was named, for she was the "victory" of her parents, Russian by blood but American in nature. Sadly, Victoria's mother passed before seeing her daughter capture that dream. So did Irina's.

Victoria started prepping for their dishes in the morning, hauling out what containers of ingredients she could find the night before. On golubtsy nights like this one, she stacked everything on the kitchen table before breakfast, carefully comparing and rationing her supplies to her mother's recipe. She tried not to vary from her mother's plan too much. But Irina was a different story. Always carrying a new vegetable or meat with her when she came home.

To compensate, Victoria would salt more of the ingredients than the recipe called for to make each leaf and bone stretch as far as possible over the week.

But every time Victoria lit the stove, she smelled the remnants of their household's last dish. As she was lighting the stove, she watched the tomato curds from last night's solyanka spark in the new flame. Their kitchen perpetually smelled of garlic, even when they had not been able to afford it that week or on the days when Victoria was determined to scrub it out. "It adds character," Irina would tell her, after adding another spilled soup or charred crust to their floor. Victoria looked over every stain on their familial home as she salted that morning's ingredients, remembering every recipe that did or did not bring a smile to Andrel's face or a spark of recognition to Vlad's eyes.

When Victoria and Irina were kids, they would fantasize about living together. At the time, it seemed like nothing more than a child's dream: they would marry at the same time, have kids at the same time, and raise them as partners. Their grandchildren would even visit together, too. "Our families will always be connected," Victoria promised, as if it were their destiny. For if one did not know the Berezin and Sokolov families, one would have confused them for one instead of two. However, prior to the turn of the century, their families had not shared a household. And as time had gone by, Victoria and Irina had found themselves depending on each other more and more.

Irina, by herself, was unable to produce the necessary wages to care for her father, and with Victoria frequently becoming pregnant, the extra mouth to feed would pull at the family's purse, even if it was only for a short time. So, they finally decided to bridge their homes, in hopes that it would ease the strain on both parties.

It was faster than expected, how they all fell into some sort of rhythm. Victoria rose first, preparing breakfast for the household. Then Irina, who helped the kids get dressed and ready for school. Andrel was next, preparing his things and his father-in-law's stuff for work as Boris helped Vlad get dressed. After stuffing their mouths and pockets with food, Andrel and Boris would head to the steel factory. Irina would head off with the kids shortly after. And once everyone was gone, Victoria was left with the new baby and Vlad to care for. It made all of those early and quiet moments all the more pleasant, a relied-upon sanity for Victoria.

When the salting was done, Victoria checked on the water. The family would be arriving for breakfast soon. She let her thin hand hover above the steam, estimating by her own comfort level if the temperature were right. Deciding not, she walked toward the window. Yellow skies were dispersing the gray that landed along Brighton in the morning.

On rare occasions—when the weather was pleasant, the smoke on the Hudson wasn't too strong, and the housework didn't seem overbearing—Victoria would venture out to the boardwalk with them. Occasionally the fresh air would lighten her worries, and even Vlad would seem to understand that it was a good day. When Victoria looked out at the crawling sun, she knew that it was going to be one of those good days.

But on other occasions, the fresh air would simply smear across her face, with every gust bringing to mind the cold breeze she would race against as a girl. After her English lessons, young Victoria had hopped between the stones on the street, patting out rhythms to tinker with when she reached the church.

The pianist knew to wait for her. "Какой темп сегодня?" *What pace today?* he would ask.

Young Victoria would tap her fingers along her thighs to show him.

"Три четверти," *Three-fourths,* he would inform her or, "Четыре трети," *Four-thirds,* he would say, until Victoria was old enough to know the difference.

By that time, Victoria had informally taken over for her teacher. Practicing with the congregation and playing during services, Victoria never felt more secure. She enjoyed getting in her best dress, having her mother pinch her pale cheeks alive, and hearing her father's low tenor of a voice bellow at her during services. It made every Sunday seem like a special holiday.

When the service was over, her mother would cart her around to every eligible bachelor who was there. Even if her mother had displayed her to the same man just one week prior, Victoria would be offered once more. One winter, her mother slipped down the stairs of the church and was bedridden for weeks. During that time, Andrel had joined the congregation. He was immediately enthralled by this dainty girl in a black dress at the piano; she looked like a simple extension of the instrument. Her hair would bounce between her eyes and the sheet music as she played up and down the keys. When the service had ended, Andrel had not sung one word. It wasn't until his fourth service at the church that he finally made his way up to the front, sitting directly in her music's path.

"Извините меня Мисс," *Excuse me, Miss,* Andrel said, quickly planting himself before her.

"Да?" *Yes?* Victoria asked.

"Я просто хотел тебе сказать," *I just wanted to tell you,* Andrel started, "ваша игра напоминает мне о русских концертах," *your playing reminds me of concerts at home.*

"Вы много слышали?" *Have you heard many?*

"Просто украденные моменты, когда я был мальчиком," *Just stolen moments when I was a boy.*

"Ну, вы должны будете рассказать мне о них когда-нибудь," *Well, you'll have to tell me about them sometime.*

For the next few weeks, Andrel had prepared concerts ready to talk about with her after every service. They would share the piano bench as Andrel recalled every piece he'd ever heard a second of, what key he believed it was in, where he sneaked in to hear it, and what his favorite part of the piece was. Victoria would try to replicate the sound based on his description. When she thought she would be getting close, she would write down the notes to hum to her mother later that night. And before they would retire, they'd work on getting the progression perfect so that Victoria could practice it the next day. She had hoped to play it for her mother.

Victoria had hoped for a lot of things, some dreams from a girl and some wishes as a mother. She had hoped that her mother would see her marry, that her mother would be there to help her with the kids. She had hoped to still play the piano, but could never juggle the time to practice. She had hoped to see a concert in Russia, but as the country warred against itself, that dream seemed further and further away. She had hoped to meet her husband's parents.

But with funds as restrictive as they were and the imperial family locking themselves away, playing in a symphony seemed more likely to happen than trips to or from Russia.

Nonetheless, Victoria bargained with the grocers and occasionally found cleaning work in the neighborhood. For every cent she saved, they were a cent closer to paying for Andrel's parents' tickets over. But every time Victoria became pregnant, the cents saved became the cents spent. And then they would start from scratch, again and again and again. Their family purse was stretched to the limit as it was, even with Irina's contributions. They could not afford more children, nor did they have the time and energy for more. Maybe another day, maybe sometime in the future, but not that day.

When the water bubbled, Victoria placed six eggs into the pot and one wire coat hanger. While she waited, she placed some bread to warm on the other burner and set the table. She scooped the eggs out first, laying them to cool on her family's plates. She carefully took out the wire hanger next, straightening its bent form before sitting down. She hooked her legs around either foot of the chair and pulled her skirt up. The rumor was: it should all come out, at least that's what Irina said. That Victoria should search for a red mothball, a dirty looking clump in the mess. If you didn't see it, you were still pregnant. You had to keep going if you didn't see it—that means you didn't reach it. And so, Victoria reached for it. The further she went, the more blood spilled out. But she did not see a red mothball. And couldn't reach for it anymore. Victoria's body cooled with the eggs that morning.

Irina saw her first. She immediately blocked the children, yelling "Изменение!" *Change!* Pushing them back to their room, Irina explained, "Погода, это будет хороший день, пойти изменить," *The weather, it is going to be a nice day—go change*.

As the kids shuffled out of their previous outfits, Irina ran to Andrel. "Виктория," *Victoria*, was all she needed to say. Andrel bounded down to the kitchen, slipping on her blood as he neared. He shook her and shook her, hoping to wake her, hoping he was in a bad dream. He shook her until Boris stopped him.

"Получить помощь," *Get help*, Boris told him.

Andrel pounded through the neighborhood, with her blood leaving reminders behind him.

In another room, Irina fed the children the eggs their mother had prepared for them.

Boris looked at his daughter and saw every dream she ever had sewed into the lining of her skin. The dark eyes from skipping meals for her family. The dirty nails she used to keep pristine for the piano. Her skin, which was once vibrant, wilted over the lining of her skirt. She was the crust of what she had once been.

Boris made sure to clean his daughter before anyone else saw her, attempting to return her to her former glory, her former hope. He wiped the blood from her knees and unhooked her legs, humming to her all the while the pieces she had played, the pieces that had given her life.

The police showed up an hour later. They didn't tell the family that Victoria was the fifth mother they had to take away that month.

Russian immigrant steel and mine workers outside a boarding house in the U.S., 1909.

Russian immigrant women. Top right: c. 1880-1889, middle left: 1885, bottom right: c. 1908.

Thanksgiving Day Parade, 1929

Eric Pierzchala

When I asked my father,
while we ate breakfast
in the dark, why he was
not working, I did not expect
a reply in his broken English.

To paraphrase, he said it was
about looking up, not back to what
was; to be thankful for what you'd had
this past year. He then looked at
my *kenőmájas* and said in Hungarian
there was still a month, a religious
holiday, a New Year to endure.

My father, not a man of words—
I can remember no time when
he said as many in any tongue.

                  Daybreak,
we'd made it to Broadway—
one subway, one elevated
train. There, was Felix the Cat, though
without his bag of tricks he was
not looking, today, to cause as much
trouble. His round body, a black globe,
both arms extended, left hand opened,
accepting what might fall into a rubber
paw—right hand pointing a pinky at me;
you, too?

Thinking back, was Felix surrogate
for Lady Liberty, bobbing, bouncing
in the cold wind, with four white-coated
handlers keeping him not far off
the ground?

                I see it now:
Felix's dark pupils were skyward,
focused on the up ahead, down the broad
avenue and the heavens above. "How American,"
I heard one of the newer Hungarian immigrants
shout in his accented English, his voice
for a moment drowning out the crowd, at least
in my ears. I thought: Father, too, can sound like that
when he tries too hard at English. I noted
Felix's devil ears, pointy, sharp—my younger brother
and I turned to each other and shouted
at the same moment, "He's a demon!"
"He's a demon!"—
echoing the words my grandmother said
about everything American. A man behind us
laughed. He leaned over my shoulder and said
in a Continental brogue, "You boys better watch it—
look close now, that cat's got toes." I looked at Felix's
feet, and he did. Ashamed, I looked back up at
his face—saw the cat smiling beyond the buildings,
the stores, the storefronts, the tall tenements,
the smog, the gray clouds—thought, unlike us,
here, down on the ground, Felix, he has a round,
petite nose—unlike me, my brother, my father,
my mother, my grandmother, the American
behind us; the people, standing, hemmed-in,
like cattle on sidewalks, by these temporary
barriers, which, if we cared to push together,
could easily be knocked down.

Later, and I'm not sure from
whom or where, I heard Felix; he was filled,
not with helium but with everyday air—and that
Felix, roaring trickster, got himself entangled
in power wires so that two of his four ropes
caught fire—though through it all he retained
his wide, upward smile.

A rumor also went 'round that at the end
of the parade route, the handlers had let
Felix float off in the air, as the Akron Tire
and Rubber Company had no plans ever to
deflate the cat. As I would come to know
later, those were good times in America,
the Statue on Bedloe's Island was a fine shade of green,
and Southeast Asian labor could not have been cheaper.

In the next day's afternoon paper,
there was an announcement that whoever found Felix,
when he landed, would get a special gift from Macy's—
"a top-right prize." And I wondered if there might have been
regret or guilt from the men upstairs at the Akron Tire and
Rubber Company or Macy's—how wonderfully naïve I was.

For Felix, I did not go searching with my brother.

It was not that year,
but another, maybe '31 or '32,
that we didn't have our standard
small turkey for our day-of-thanks
feast. And as our mother presented,
on our very best plate, eight boiled
hot dogs each wrapped in a piece
of Wonder Bread, she said more than
questioned (and in English, so Dad
didn't fully understand), "This year,
what could be more American?"

Felix the
Cat, 1927.

162

And Yet You Do Not Vote
(*Henry David Thoreau*)

Marion Avrilyn Jones

I envy you. You're odd. Around nature,
you are tender and devoted. You envy no one.

Naïve in your youth, you are devoured
in hard rain on dry dirt, and you thrive.

You dote on trees, on ant and deer,
on vein and artery, on every heart.

You dote on a hare, on a horned toad.
You yearn to dive into a river, a hidden ravine.

You dote on honey and endeavor, even on death.
You enter into your errand, and you never deviate.

You dote on the untidy earth in and around you.
You are true. You are our author, and you endure.

The daunted, the hurt, the tired read your every idea
and are united. You are never done. You do not die.

You'd rather haunt your tiny, verdant Eden
than have an ornate throne in vaunted heaven.

You hate the adorned, the hoarder. You hate
the train, heavy iron threaded on untried terrain.

You hate a duty on your head or heart.
You hate—you hate!—the dread trade.

You are rare. You are thunder. Thorn and air
are in you. A hut, a route north, a raid are in you.

Sympathy

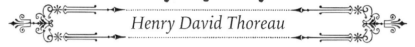

Henry David Thoreau

Written on June 24, 1839 (all sic).

Lately alas I knew a gentle boy,
  Whose features all were cast in Virtue's mould,
As one she had designed for Beauty's toy,
  But after manned him for her own stronghold.

On every side he open was as day,
  That you might see no lack of strength within,
For walls and ports do only serve alway
  For a pretence to feebleness and sin.

Say not that Caesar was victorious,
  With toil and strife who stormed the House of Fame;
In other sense this youth was glorious,
  Himself a kingdom wheresoe'er he came.

No strength went out to get him victory,
  When all was income of its own accord;
For where he went none other was to see,
  But all were parcel of their noble lord.

He forayed like the subtle breeze of summer,
  That stilly shows fresh landscapes to the eyes,
And revolutions worked without a murmur,
  Or rustling of a leaf beneath the skies.

So was I taken unawares by this,
  I quite forgot my homage to confess;
Yet now am forced to know, though hard it is,
  I might have loved him, had I loved him less.

Each moment, as we nearer drew to each,
A stern respect withheld us farther yet,
So that we seemed beyond each other's reach,
And less acquainted than when first we met.

We two were one while we did sympathize,
So could we not the simplest bargain drive;
And what avails it now that we are wise,
If absence doth this doubleness contrive?

Henry
David
Thoreau,
1861.

Eternity may not the chance repeat,
But I must tread my single way alone,
In sad remembrance that we once did meet,
And know that bliss irrevocably gone.

The spheres henceforth my elegy shall sing,
For elegy has other subject none;
Each strain of music in my ears shall ring
Knell of departure from that other one.

Make haste and celebrate my tragedy;
With fitting strain resound ye woods and fields;
Sorrow is dearer in such case to me
Than all the joys other occasion yields.

Is't then too late the damage to repair?
Distance, forsooth, from my weak grasp hath reft
The empty husk, and clutched the useless tare,
But in my hands the wheat and kernel left.

If I but love that virtue which he is,
Though it be scented in the morning air,
Still shall we be dearest acquaintances,
Nor mortals know a sympathy more rare.

Two Truths and a Lie

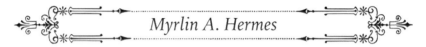

Myrlin A. Hermes

London, 1668.

Nelly Gwynn and I play Two Truths and a Lie while I pluck the hairs from 'twixt her thighs. She will have no one else but me to do it, and I think 'tis less my steady hand she prefers than the steady stream of stories I keep up to distract her from the tweezers' sting.

"I was trained in barbering at my father's knee," I say, plucking a long, gold strand out from the underside of hers. "He was a famous *chirurgeon* of Canterbury. Not famous for his surgery, mind you, for his hands would shake most terribly, except when he was drinking. But he was known all over the city for telling the best tales." I shrug. "Well, tallest, anyway. If only he could find a way to sell hot air, my mother always said, we should be as rich as Croesus."

"She must have loved him." To Nelly, now and always, everything comes down to love. She is lying naked on the rug before my fire, her skin still damp and slightly flushed from her weekly bath (Mr. Killigrew insists, especially now that the King has been sending for her).

I give a noncommittal grunt. "He spent her dowry all on tulip bulbs."

He'd said he knew a man who knew a man in Amsterdam who would pay him his own weight in gold for a single flower. He showed them to her in his open hands like magic beans. "This one, Lizzie," he'd said, holding up something resembling a blighted chestnut, an undersized onion. "This is our country manor." He held up another. "And this, our house in town. And this, a coach-and-four—one of those new ones, with the springs—to carry us from one house to the other, dressed in our fine brocades and silks."

"Ah, well," I sigh now, shaking my head. "At least they still looked pretty in the spring, blooming in the window boxes of our rooms above the Barbershop."

Nelly pouts at my cynicism. "Have you never been in love, Aphra?"

"Aye, many times." I fix my attentions on another curly, fair hair, this one a little higher than the knee. "The last one ended badly."

She nods in sympathy. "He broke your heart?"

"I shot him with a pistol."

"What?!"

I yank the hair, while she's already yelping. "Well, I did not say I *hit* him. I was not even aiming for him, not really. And anyway, if I *had* killed him, it should have been no more than justice served, for 'twas not just me he had betrayed with his double-crossings, but his King and Country, as well!" I tilt my head to the side and purse my lips, considering. "Oh—and I suppose also his wife."

At a nudge from my elbow Nelly parts her legs a little more. The Duke's Playhouse is bigger than ours and has better *Sceneries*, which move on pulleys to fly in from the wings. Moll Davis, at the Duke's House, has the sweetest voice in all of Covent Garden, and they say no one can match her grace for dancing. But here at the King's House, we have *heart*.

And of course, by *heart*, I mean Nelly.

And of course, by *Nelly*, I mean Nelly's legs.

Killigrew knows the audiences do not pack the pit and swell the boxes full every night to see her sing or dance or (Heaven help us) *act*, but rather to see *her*. Nelly as a saucy pageboy, Nelly as a cherub, Nelly as a saucy maid in disguise as a pageboy or cherub— any excuse, really, to get her into breeches.

With a twitch of my wrist, I pluck a long strand from just below the swell of her fleshy rump, holding this pubic miracle up to the light. No embroiderer ever threaded needle with so fine a golden wire, not even for the Queen's own wedding gown.

Nelly hisses in pain. I lick my fingertip and slip it up her thigh to where the hair grows coarse and coppery. My tweezers do not venture up so high (Killigrew dares not show any more Nelly, lest the Puritans riot again), but my bare hand snakes up between the rosy lips, which part at my touch, pearlescent and sea-damp as the opening of a conch.

I once saw a conch-shell trumpeted like a horn by a sailor, who blew it hard upon the end; but this particular instrument, I have found, is more like to the flageolet, and best played trippingly on the tip of the tongue. Spreading my fingers wide, I bend my face between her thighs, tickling the tender reed until I have articulated from her a pretty arpeggio of notes. Her legs are famous throughout all of London, to the very uppermost crook of her dimpled thigh; but *this* view is reserved for royalty.

And me.

"Ay, Aphra!" she gives a long sigh at last, relaxing back onto the tattered tiger skin. "Tell me, where did you learn *that*? Not in a Barbershop, I'll warrant."

I cast her a sideways grin. "Oh, the usual school for girls in such matters—a convent. Did you not know I had been intended for a nun?"

"You?" she howls. "Nay, *that* must be the Lie."

"Well, I never said I was a *good* nun," I admitted, wiping my chin dry on my sleeve. "In fact, I may well have been the worst novitiate in the history of the Benedictine order."

She throws her head back, laughing—like church bells, such as one used to hear pealing all through London on a Sunday morning, back before the Fire melted 'em. The laugh that reaches all the way up to tickle the ears of the topmost gallery. I think Nelly's laugh may be even more famous than her legs.

Sitting back on my heels, I survey my handiwork: from thigh to ankle, smooth and golden-white as clotted cream. How could a thousand Moll Davises ever compete with that?

Women at war are different from men. A man would never seek the company of his worst enemy unless they were about to come to blows. But friendship is the female battlefield. Everyone knows the King has sent for Nelly; and everyone knows exactly what that means. Everyone knows Moll Davis would prefer to be the sole Actress in the King's vast Armada of Mistresses. So, when Moll sent word that she would pay Nelly a visit this afternoon "for tea," everyone understood 'twas less a social call than an opening salvo, shot straight across the bow.

"She is just coming to wave around that giant diamond ring he bought her," Nell grumbles, "and boast about how she has been summoned to share the King's bed tonight, and ride with him in his coach tomorrow when the court sets out for Tunbridge Wells." She sulks. "I wish I were the one going on holiday with him. I wish I had some magic spell to ruin her in his eyes forever."

And because I, too, am in love with Nelly, I would make her every wish come true. Even if the magic that has suddenly occurred to me should be more in the vein of wicked imp or puckish sprite than fairy godmother.

Bidding her wait a minute, I go into the other room (I have only the two, and even these are dear enough to let, in Covent Garden). My old sea-chest is by now well-stained with layered spills of ink and wine and candlewax, for in my travels it has often served as both writing desk and dining table. Inside, I keep those relics that have managed to survive with me all these years, against fire, shipwreck, prison, and the pawnbroker: a shagreen toolcase, to which I return the long tweezers, sliding them into their place 'twixt razors, crisping irons, and lancets for bloodletting; those playscripts I have written (which Mr. Killigrew still refuses to stage, on account of my sex); and, wrapped in the tatters of a gown by now so threadbare you could hardly tell that it had once been green, or velvet, my diary.

It once had been Papa's old Accounts book, its figures diligently rubbed out with a pouncing stone for me to overwrite with my adventures. By now, it is so stuffed with contracts, papers, IOUs, official documents, and lists of secret spy-codes, it fans open like a bellows, and its cover is mottled with black mildew spots, still remaining from its days in the perpetual tropical damp. At last, I find what I was looking for, wrapped in the cloth: an unimpressive, wrinkled, gray-brown lump. Returning to the other room, I offer this unappetizing truffle to Nelly, who (alas) has by this time returned herself into her clothes. Her bodice laces in front, so she can do it up herself; even the King's whore, after all, is still a whore.

"Did you get those French sweetmeats Moll likes, to serve with the tea?" I ask.

Nelly rolls her eyes. "Aye—and a pretty penny they cost, too. Her tastes have grown dear since the days when she was just another Actress, like the rest of us."

I bite my tongue and do not remind her that the 'rest of us' are not all Actresses, nor how much better *her* position pays per week than that of general *amanuensis*, agony aunt and *factotum* of the playhouse. "Well, grind up this root in a mortar and pestle fine, like cinnamon, and sprinkle the dust over those cakes you plan to serve to Mrs. Davis," I instruct her. "But take care, if you are wise, not to eat any of it yourself."

"You think I should poison her?" For a moment, Nelly looks as if she might actually be considering it. Eighteen, starry-eyed, and ambitious is a reckless combination, as I do well recall.

"Go to! 'Tis no poison!" I tilt my head from side to side. "Well, not *exactly* poison. Just the root of the Jalap flower—a very pretty vine. It grows in the Amazon jungles, and the Natives there make good use of it, when suffering from constipation. But take too much, and you'll be suffering, rather, from a *lack* of constipation." I grin, watching as Nelly takes my meaning and colors up with scandalized delight. "She'll be perfectly all right in a few days. But I do not think His Majesty will look the same on Moll tomorrow morning—nor his silken sheets!"

Nelly squeals her thanks, covering my face with kisses. "Where did you find such an exotic drug? I've not seen it before in an apothecary's shop."

"Oh, you know." I shrug modestly. "Here and there, in my travels. That was from the time—nay, I must tell the whole story someday—I ended up leading a rebellion of African slaves! And all because the King of 'em was so handsome—as black as ebony, and extremely large in the . . ." I give a coy wink. "But *that* is a tale for another day."

Nelly laughs again, that gravelly, infectious belly laugh I'd rather hear than Moll Davis' clear soprano singing me the sweetest lullaby. "Aye, Aphra," she teases. "And tell me, was that before or after the time you were forced to marry with the pirate?"

I shrug. I have a reputation to maintain, after all, as an inveterate exaggerator. Around the Theater, the young players all think I am a bit dotty—Mrs. Aphra Behn, everyone's eccentric widowed aunt who's had a drop of sherry. "Tell us again about the time you met the Indians," they will beg after a few down at the Rose. And as long as they are willing to refill my cup, I'm happy to oblige.

"Well, for one thing, Mr. Dryden has got them all wrong in his play," I inform them, "and Mrs. Marshall is wearing the princess' headdress backwards. . . ."

They all laugh at my tales, and praise the telling; but by their winks and smirks across the table, I know 'tis not the ignorance of Dryden nor Ann Marshall, but the batty old bawd who imagines she has met an Amazon, who is the real butt of their joke.

But every true tale stands between two falsehoods, each looking on it from the other side. And in every lie a person can invent, two truths will be revealed. So, if Nelly never presses me to tell which of my tall tales is the lie (thinking they all are), neither do I ever confess. She never would believe me anyway, if I told her every last story was true.

Well, true enough, at least.

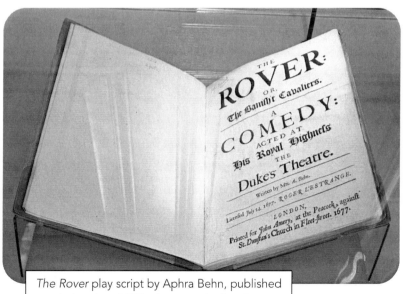

The Rover play script by Aphra Behn, published in London, 1677, photographed at the Huntington Botanical Garden, San Marino, California, in June 2023.

The Dream

Aphra Behn

Written c. 1680.

All trembling in my arms Aminta lay,
Defending of the bliss I strove to take;
Raising my rapture by her kind delay,
Her force so charming was and weak.
The soft resistance did betray the grant,
While I pressed on the heaven of my desires;
Her rising breasts with nimbler motions pant;
Her dying eyes assume new fires.
Now to the height of languishment she grows,
And still her looks new charms put on;
Now the last mystery of Love she knows,
We sigh, and kiss: I waked, and all was done.

'Twas but a dream, yet by my heart I knew,
Which still was panting, part of it was true:
Oh how I strove the rest to have believed;
Ashamed and angry to be undeceived!

Engraving of Aphra Behn
after a lost portrait by
John Riley, c. 1680.

A Walk to Lafayette

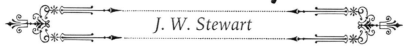

J. W. Stewart

I wanted to work, needed to, but the uneven click-clack of the typewriters was worrying. There was nothing especially peculiar in the punctuated din of the office, yet it felt off. Rows and columns of desks formed an orderly grid with each identical wood desk supplied with gray typewriter, piles of papers both blank and full, and a government employee like me. The phone in our boss' office would ring from time to time. Muffled discussions later become announcements and changes in policy from the diminutive man in charge, the young cousin of a Nevada senator.

I didn't have a senator cousin, so I didn't have my own office or title. I transcribed data, typed up reports, and stared at the light-blue walls and dirty windows. A milk production spreadsheet lay on my desk; the man's shaky penciled numbers were maddening. I cursed at the many men I'd never meet for their halfhearted scratches and carelessness with facts.

My father's very modest connections got me the job, and I was thankful for it and for the escape. I'd eagerly left home for college, and once finished, harbored no desire to return. I wasn't political and had no interest in farm policy, but the position was far from Indiana. Washington, D.C., was lively, noisy, and removed from the quiet weight of my family. Most of those I had met made life more bearable; some made it painful.

I rarely wrote home. Every time I tried, the words seemed too distant and without the requisite longing for home others expressed. I found nothing inside to muster an honest *I miss home* or an *I miss you*. I knew I'd have to lie to them a great deal, and I do enough of that as I worry through the day. It's tiresome. Silence is better than a lie, which is better than the truth in my case.

Not even twenty-four hours had passed since my afternoon meeting two floors up. Only my neighbor to my right noticed my absence for those hours; her graying eyes behind black glasses damned me for the absence and for a general sense of laziness. She'd been in the office since '34, one of the first. I never responded to her glancing admonitions or her questions about what I did during the war. No one needed to hear my story.

"Meeting" was a rather odd euphemism for the hours in that quiet room on one of the other floors, but it was my only explanation: "I had a meeting." I glanced up from my desk and looked for the gossiping jackals among the oblivious.

Yesterday's meeting started with the summons from a higher floor and the easiest of questions.

"It's Bill, right?" he had asked.

He had gravity about him, tall, athletic, in a well-pressed navy suit. The pinstripes were a delicate touch. I assumed his wife picked it out. I sat, then he sat. He placed his cigarettes and gold lighter on the table and waited for an answer. I told him yes and added the rest of my name. He pulled at his nose, giving no notice to my answer, and continued. His hair rose and fell in precise shiny strands; the faint hint of pomade worked its way through the heavy aftershave. It was a virile but unsettling smell.

"I'm Stan Dweyer," he said. His voice was dry, cutting.

Stan shoved his hand toward me. I did what I do with everything; I hesitated and then slid my smaller hand into Stan's. His touch was warm and increasingly firm, tightened until I felt the slightest discomfort, and then he released me. I wondered if I cringed.

"Let's make sure I have the right file. Just a second."

Stan dug through his briefcase, glancing toward me as his fingers thumbed through the crumple and pop of bureaucratic paper. I again let my eyes roam around the windowless conference room and away from Stan. I had never been in this particular room, yet, like most of the building, everything was indistinguishable from one floor to the next.

Drawing forth a large, brown folder, Stan dropped it onto the table, flipped it open, and then looked up at me. He offered a thin smile, but I held back any instinct to return the expression. My foot bounced, keeping time with the situation. The soft pulsing of my shoes was the only sound in the otherwise stale room. My stomach turned and ached.

Stan went on with simple questions: Where ya from? Where'd you go to college? What are your parents like? Stan only glanced up briefly with each question. I responded. My answers felt like the lines of a script, a prelude to what he needed. Stan wrote nothing, didn't even pick up the pen.

"Been in D.C. a year now. You made any friends?" Stan asked.

He raised his eyes directly to mine. I stared back, taking in another of Stan's curious smiles, a look that most would assume was an offer of friendship, a gesture to calm. His sharp features supported his blue eyes. They were impossible not to look at. My foot continued to keep time. I told him of a few friends from work. Stan nodded his head, his hand and pen held still.

"You know a George Fischer?"

I pretended not to recognize the name and lied as simply as possible. The names of the few people I'd met since coming to Washington slipped around my mind. I hated hearing their names; I knew the danger that comes from having people like Stan know your name. I tried never to say them aloud. Stan's name grew in my mind and pressed outward.

"What about Thomas Durrand? You know him?"

Stan tossed the dark-brown folder aside. He looked at me and let his eyes trail up and down, seeking what I was barely hiding. I knew I looked pathetic in his eyes, which is what I'm sure he wanted.

I lied again. Thomas was a good man who didn't deserve to be punished. I tried not to let his name sit in my mind for too long. Stan smiled at my deceit again, this time broader and more intense, glee more than calming or friendly. I wondered then if he knew how much the question and the lie hurt me, if that was the point. Cut me so I eventually bleed out what he wants.

Stan leaned back in his chair. The grinding of springs and joints of the metal dug into the silence.

"So, what did you do this past Thursday after work? Thursday the twelfth."

Stan stretched his arms above himself, increasing his large presence, and then slid his hands behind his head, his thick fingers intertwining in comfort, all of it mocking me. The mention of Thursday summoned the anxiety I lived with, a shaking in my nerves and worry deep in my kidneys. Stan leaned back against the weight of the chair because that's what he was supposed to do. I was intended to cringe and lie. We both did our jobs.

We sat motionless. I did not have to search for new fabrications; they were built long ago. No new details were needed. Stan dropped the casual attitude, the professional disinterest. His widening grin was back, his cheeks flush, and his eyes wide. He was building toward my most important lie.

The legs of Stan's chair scraped against the linoleum floor, the cutting sound distracting me from my well-practiced deceptions. He circled the table, and his navy suit now hovered behind me. I felt his hands grip my shoulders—not squeezing, but more a gentle, urging massage. The wool coat and silk shirt ground against each other and my skin, rough and hot. I stared forward, could see the hint of our reflection in the smudged glass, a hovering mass of blue and strength and my own spectral look below.

"OK, bub. A young . . . handsome . . . boy like yourself must have had plans that night. Surely, you weren't just sitting in that drab room alone? Or maybe you were home but not alone?" Stan asked.

"No one's ever been in my room. It's not allowed," I pleaded while still practicing my answer to the previous question in my head.

"Yeah, that's what Mrs. Schorr at the rooming house said. You just leave in the morning and come home after dinner. A nice, quiet, young boy is how she described you. Are you, Bill? Are you a nice . . . quiet . . . young . . . boy?" Stan's lips popped and lingered with each 'boy.'

I winced, hated that he had talked to my landlady. *Who else had he spoken to?* I wondered but never asked. I felt Stan's breathing on my right ear, and I wanted to scream, claw at the table, and beg to leave. It was a familiar feeling in my life, so I ignored it.

"I suppose," I said. "I just try to do my job, do good."

This time I told some of the truth that didn't involve Thomas and George or anyone else.

Stan's mouth retreated away, and his hands slipped down over my shoulders. He gave me a quick, fatherly pat on each arm with his large hands. They seemed to grow each time they touched me. "You never answered my question, Bill." His breath was now on my left ear. "Seems like you avoided it. You're not being unhelpful, are you? Mrs. Schorr also says you take walks at night. You like walking at night?" His voice slipped to a whisper when he asked about the walks.

My eyes slipped closed and tightened.

"I happen to know you try to be very helpful," he continued, "a pleaser if you will. I knew lots of smarty-pants boys like you back in school, even a few during the war, always so very helpful. You want to please me, don't you, Bill?"

"Yes, sir, I want to, but—" That was the truth even though I wish it wasn't.

"That's good, Bill. Now, what did you do that night? Where did you go, pal?"

Both of Stan's hands were again on my shoulders. He squeezed, worked me toward the next lie. He wanted me to lie, to shake and choke on it. Then we'd get to the little bit of truth he actually needed.

Thursday the twelfth was five days before Stan pulled me into that office. I ventured out into the city that night, once an exception but now part of my routine. I walked quickly, the hint of cold made more prominent by the speed of my steps and the breeze in my face. Traffic was light. With dinner over for most, the swarms of government workers were home readying for the next day. Like most of my coworkers, my routine was simple: breakfast, work, lunch, work, an early dinner, then home. At home I found comfort: book in my lap, the radio on most nights. If I cranked my head just so from my chair, I could see the lights of the Capitol through my window. Then my routine changed on a whim, then changed out of need.

I felt my own footfalls, the click of my shoes announcing my presence at a moment begging for anonymity. Turning left onto 16th Street, I found only a few others slipping on and off the sidewalks. Rhode Island, Massachusetts, then M Street. I turned my head to find the red-brick church, softly lit, standing out among the darkened offices. My stride quickened through L, K, and I streets.

Shimmers of shadows and lamplight filled the paths stretching into Lafayette Park. It never seemed fully lit, a darkened den in the middle of the city. I took the path to the left, never the path to the right. My feet and eyes searched through the familiar place always made alien by the darkness and my own anxiety.

After finding the bench, I gently sat down as wood creaked and grated against my back. I listened more closely and found the hushed voices, the quick and still steps, the furtive chirps of restless birds. My legs fidgeted in the chill. Pushing and pulling the loose gravel under my feet, I squirmed until I realized how loud it all was. I stopped. A young couple walked past but didn't notice me. I forced a short smile and nodded to be polite, nevertheless. Their attention was drawn inward, their wool coats grinding against each other, their arms tightly knotted. Then nothing but stillness for the longest time. It thrilled me to wait for something you know will happen eventually.

I heard the steps, singular and slow, a little before eleven. He stopped a few feet from me, and then I felt the sounds of creaking wood against my back. We sat in silence, each of us breathing slowly, looking in all directions but one. He towered over me in his coat and hat. I smelled the pungent sweet menthol of Pinaud.

"A nice night," came the solid voice from my side.

The evening grew even colder. Low clouds hid the stars, giving the city a hazy hue. Yet, I agreed with a single soft word. I turned toward him and waited. His head turned toward me, still faceless through the shadows, but I knew sculpted lines and smooth features were what I could not see. His hand fell into my lap, the slow undulations of his fingers in complete control. He grabbed my left hand and slid it between the heavy flaps of his coat. He let out a deep sigh and a cloud of steam into the park as my own fingers found their way through the layers of cloth. His hands swallowed me and forced me to do what I wanted. His length flowed through my hand, burned itself into my flushed palm. The anxiety of the open park slipped away in our rhythmic movement. My eyes closed, and I tried to please him. His knuckles flexed and tightened, controlling the pace and tightness of my grip. He held me tighter, pushing pain into my pleasure. He grunted through gritted teeth that I could see in the moonlight. His body shook and silently flung itself rigid against the bench.

He was up and leaning down into my ear before I could right myself. He whispered a thank you and a wish to see what I had for him next time. His lips barely graced my cheek when he pulled away and walked slowly back from where he came.

I left the park behind and hurried home, sliding my left hand up to my nose and inhaling. The familiar smell of sweat and soap filled my mind and quickened my steps.

I told Stan again that I went for a walk. Walks ease my restlessness, and the statue of Lafayette is beautiful at night, I explained. The buttons of his jacket pressed into my back as he leaned into me. He gripped me harder when I lied, gently shook me in agitation. It was like his arms, chest, and face were crawling over me, trying to swallow me up. I tensed and tried to slow my breathing.

I looked back at him for the first time, met those blue eyes, and was instantly sorry. Stan shook his head and narrowed his brow. The next question slowly slipped out of a disapproving grin.

"Are you a homosexual, Bill?"

I audibly choked, seized up. Death had always been more appealing than hearing that word. Stan knew it, too. I mumbled in confusion, clearly off-script from my life. "I don't know what you mean."

"A fairy? A GOD DAMN homosexual, Bill? Were you looking for another homosexual in the park that night? Were you looking for some strong man to make you his? To take you back to that pathetic apartment and make you into a woman?"

Stan's voice urged and twisted in me. I felt like his rough hands were gripping my stomach, the fleshy bits slipping between his fingers. My denials were drowned out by Stan's deep and rich timbre of hateful words.

"I didn't figure you for a fairy, Bill. A hardworking father who's a former Navy man, two brothers in the Corps, a swell mom. How could they have raised a fairy? I looked at your file and said, no, he can't possibly be a delicious little homosexual, not Bill."

I pleaded with him, lied through my teeth, and he began to laugh. I hated when he laughed. He wanted to see me beg, so I begged. His hands moved up my shoulders until they were almost around my neck; his fingers slid against the collar of my shirt. I repeatedly said no, but it didn't matter.

"That's what I told everyone: no way Bill's a homosexual, but why were you in that park, at that hour?"

He wasn't choking me, but I was out of words. It was all his show from then on. My body was deflating, sweating against my suit, my pants tight with unwanted excitement brought on by hate, hate for him and everyone that wondered about me.

"Listen, someone in your office is a homosexual. There's been talk, lots of talk. Stories of some damn immoral stuff. We can't have that. No sir, we can't have that kind of stuff here, Bill."

Why does he insist on saying my name like that? Good God, stop, get to the ending, I thought. My mind screamed with wonderful immoral stuff. I thought of George and Thomas and enjoyed the punishing weight of Stan's hands.

I told him I needed air, a break. He ignored my weakness.

"If not you, then who, Bill? You seem an astute young guy, top of your class, a real man of the office. Whom should I be talking to, if not you?"

I could hear him mocking me, making me small in his hands, as he got to the final point. A name came to my mind I knew would satisfy him. A simple name would give us both what we wanted.

The office hummed in anticipation of lunch. I waited and wondered if anyone could see my anxiety. Margerie stood up, a rare movement in the deskbound office, and walked to Jean's desk. They managed the office, kept the paper flowing. The two spoke softly as I looked down, looked busy. The corner of my eye kept watch. The buzz from the clock behind me crawled about my ears and drowned out the two women. Margerie looked my way. I began typing, adding my own irregular click-clack to the room. I tried to find an inconspicuous rhythm. I knew they'd hear it if I were typing weirdly. I wondered why all of them were doing this to me.

I should have written home more. I pushed away at the persistent stray thought, but my mind insisted. *What would you have told them? About the quiet nights in the boardinghouse? The endless hours of rearranging jumbled numbers into meaningful yet pointless words, justifying policy edicts from the office with the frosted glass.* I looked around and could see my boss moving behind that glass now. I wondered if the news trickled in to him yet.

Maybe mention how Margerie had invited you to join her family for dinner and how you declined? Oh, I know a good story you could include in a letter to your sweet old mom. Perhaps regale them of running into Sue, your supervisor's secretary and her roommate at the Keith after seeing Beat the Devil. *There's a juicy story your mother would love.* I grinned at my own little joke. *Remember her pretty roommate, how she nervously fidgeted when you ran into them. You marveled at the sharp contrast between Sue's blond hair and pale skin with the rich browns of her roommate's hair and Mediterranean skin. Remember how you guys stood outside casually discussing Gina Lollobrigida. Your parents would never see that movie, so they wouldn't care about that part of the story. Maybe you could explain the furtive touch between the hands of the two young women as they walked away or how you stood watching to see if it happened again, wanting it to happen again. You think the parents would enjoy that scandalous little story? Maybe you could invent some details to give both your sweet, old parents heart attacks? Remember the look on Sue's face a few days later when she brought you leftover pot roast. You clearly saw in her eyes a plea for understanding, a plea for silence. You could tell Mom that the roast was not as good as hers was. Yes, Mom would like that much better than the filthy little stories of what her son and his coworkers have been up to while doing their patriotic duty.*

I stopped typing and twisted my neck, trying to rid my head of my own voice. I wish I could make myself quiet.

My eyes oscillated between the penciled-in numbers to my right and the office, my fingers darting and striking as my eyes did the same. *Jean and Margerie never talk—why are they talking? Well, they sometimes talk, right? Is this a one or a seven? Damn this man's bad handwriting.* I needed to concentrate, but everything seemed set on tormenting me. Maybe I deserved it.

The clock droned on as lunchtime approached, when everyone would stream downstairs. I usually left early to avoid the crowds, the uncomfortable small talk, and the questions. The itch from wanting to know kept me seated.

Chairs squeaked and swiveled at the far end of the room. I cringed as I heard what caught everyone's attention. Above the buzzing of the clock and the slowing click-clack of typewriters, I heard the light sobbing sliding down the hallway. The tears grew louder, punctuated by shuffling feet and the dual steps of authority matching tone and tempo. Several others stood, clutching collars and pearls. I refused to look. I focused on the disapproving faces of Margerie and Jean. I cataloged every frown and wrinkle of shock in their faces from what I already knew. Sue was being led down the drab, narrow hallway to the iron elevator at the end.

The crying was now just outside our office. I refused to look at her and at the men who would be taking her away. Maybe Stan was on one side of Sue—I never knew. Yet, my thoughts would not let me get away with not seeing; they imagined the smeared makeup and sorrowful eyes as her secrets found light and she was fired. I saw in the darkness of my mind some man's hand wrapped tightly around Sue's pale skin, the grip bringing a flush of blood to the surface. I have similar imagined scenes for Thomas and George that never left me. I had heard they were silent as they were led away. Sue sobbed uncontrollably.

The crying faded as the elevator closed, and the gears sent her downward. *If I didn't say something, someone else would. She was being too obvious. I had to give Stan something. I wanted to give Stan something.* I wrenched the real from the rationalization. Margerie and Jean talked in whispered disgust while they gathered their coats and purses for lunch.

The next day was Thursday. I worked and ignored the constant chatter in the office. Sue would be everyone's topic. Heated gossip and feigned concerns for families always lasted a few days and then were pushed out of polite conversation. It was that way with Thomas and George. No one even spoke their names now, except Stan. He liked saying their names to me, watching me flinch.

After work, I slipped down the steps of my apartment to meet the night a little earlier. The cold had driven most of the nice people from the park. I waited on the bench. I knew Stan would never be early. I would hear his feet exactly when I was supposed to, and then I'd see him on Thursday precisely when he wanted me to, and our little game would start over again. Stan liked our game; it earned him a raise and promotion.

It was dropping into the fifties that night, but I held on and listened to the rustling of the trees. I shook from the cold and anticipation. It's always exciting to wait for something you know for certain is going to happen.

400 More Homosexuals Ousted from Gov't Jobs

D. C. March 25.—A prompt drive to kid

Throughout the 1940s and 50s, thousands of LGBTQ+ government employees and military serviceworkers lost their jobs during the Lavender Scare, a purging of "sexual perversion" from the U.S. government by senators and U.S. officials. While making front page news in the 40s and 50s, a quieter purging of LGBTQ+ employees in the government continued well into the new millennium, with the HIV AIDS epidemic of the 80s and 90s exacerbating an already panicked and ignorant witch hunt.

Frank Kameny (middle front), an early LGBTQ+ activist who lost his job in 1957 for being gay, leads a protest in front of the White House in 1965, the largest public demonstration for gay rights in world history at the time.

183

After the Hostile Takeover, 1990

Laura Budofsky Wisniewski

F ar from New York City,
in a field to the north of the river
a man met the gaze of a bobcat.

Between them,
an acre of switchback flared gold.
The hum of toil stilled.

> He'd leveraged the surprise buyout
> with a seven-figure blind pool
> gutting the last of the holdouts.

Hay fern, deer musk, and blue stem,
heavy and familiar,
scented the cooling air.

The bobcat,
its tufted ears flickering like thoughts,
crouched in the dusking field.

> But the man,
> soiled with the sweat of the boardroom
> dulled by the second martini,

> was afraid of the shadows between things
> of the lift of hairs on his body
> of the ghost in the dew as it fell.

Lynnhaven River, 1706

Chelsea Bunn

> . . . *Grace Sherwood was convicted at a trial that*
> *saw her thrown into the Lynnhaven River with*
> *her thumbs tied to her feet. . . . The rules of the*
> *trial were simple: If you floated, you were guilty*
> *of being a witch; if you sank, you were cleared.*
> *And dead. Sherwood floated. She served more*
> *than seven years in jail, was released and lived*
> *until she was 80. She is the only person con-*
> *victed in Virginia by a "witch ducking trial."*
> —Washington Post, July 12, 2006

What I want is the sanctuary
            of wide salt marshes,
      sweet seashore mallow shooting
from its crown of roots,
            and oysters
                  filtering the mudflats,
      the calcite of their bivalve shells
                  cementing shut their sex.
      But you've drug me here
through milkweed and inkberry
                  from jail
to water—pure element—
to decide if I've bewitched your hogs and cotton fields,
      blighted garden and ovum.
                  Examine me for proof
      and find nothing
            but my widow skin, soft as shadows,
and the dark marks you think you see,
      which each of our three sons
                  deepened from within my womb and which

my husband kissed.
Bind me
    thumb to toe and throw
  my body in
                    you know
            I have been sinful
but I've been decent too
            and in the brackish deep I see
                    your God and your God
        makes of me a hollow thing
                and carries me to shore
        and turns the bright sky
                    black and gold with cloudburst and I wait
for you to adorn me
        with allium
                and rosemary and a masked
                    animal
cast me in bronze
    and stand before me
trembling, wet.

A 17th-century engraving of ducking (or "ordeal by water"), similar to what would have been the punishment for Grace Sherwood, accused of healing the sick with herbs.

THE CHARTER OAK AWARD
First Place
BEST HISTORICAL

The Case of Grace Sherwood

Princess Anne County Court

Editor's Note: Transcription of selected proceedings of the Princess Anne County Court hearings, 1706, as transcribed by historian George Lincoln Burr in 1914. The case first went to the county court, then general court, then back to the county court; and while there are indications that the case went back again to the general court, there are no records remaining from that time. Some spelling has been modernized and uncommon contractions have been expanded for ease of reading; anything that is understandable as-is has been left sic.

Princess Ann sessions. At a Court held the 3d of January 1706.

Whereas Luke Hill and uxor [wife][1] Summoned Grace Sherwood to this Court in Suspetion of witchcraft and she fayling to appear, it is therefore ordered that attachment to the Sheriff do Issue to Attach her body to answer the said Summons next court.

February 6, 1706

Suite for Suspition of witchcraft brought by Luke Hill against Grace Sherwood is ordered to be referr till to morrow.

February 7, 1706

Whereas a Complaint was brought against Grace Sherrwood on Suspition of witchcraft by Luke Hill, etc.: and the matter being after a long time debated and ordered that the said Hill pay all fees of this Complaint and that the said Grace be here next Court to be Searched according to the Complaint by a Jury of women to decide

187

the said Difference: and the Sheriff is Likewise ordered to Summon an able Jury accordingly.

March 7, 1706

Whereas a Complaint have been [made] to this Court by Luke Hill and his wife that one grace Sherrwood of this County was and Have been a Long time Suspected of witchcraft and have been as Such Represented wherefore the Sheriff at the last Court was ordered to Summon a Jury of women to this Court to Serch her on the said Suspicion, She assenting to the Same. And after the Jury was impannelld and Sworn and Sent out to make Due inquirery and Inspection into all Cercumstances, After a Mature Consideracion They bring in this verditt: wee of the Jury have Serchtt Grace Sherwood and have found Two things like titts with Severall other Spotts. . . .[2]

May 2, 1706

Whereas a former Complaint was brought against Grace Sherwood for Suspicion of Witchcraft, which by the Atturney Generall Report to his Excellency in Councill was too Generall and not Charging her with any perticular Act, therefore represented to them that Princess Ann Court might if they thought fitt have her examined De Novo, and the Court Being of Oppinion that there is great Cause of Suspicion Doe therefore order that the Sheriff take the Said Grace into his Safe Costody untill She Shall give bond and Security for her Appearance to the next Court to be examined Denovo and that the Constable of that precinkt go with the Sheriff and Serch the Said graces House and all Suspicious places Carfully for all Images and Such like things as may any way Strengthen The Suspicion, and it is likewise Ordered that the Sheriff Summon an Able

 Jury of Women, also all Evidences as Cann give in anything against her in Evidence, in behalf of our Soveraign Lady the Queen, To Attend the next Court Accordingly.

June 6, 1706

Whereas Grace Sherwood of this County have been Complained of as a person Suspected of Witchcraft, and now being Brought before this Court in order for examinacion, this Court have therefore requested mr Maximillian Boush to present Informacion against her as Councill in behalf of our Soveraign Lady the Queen in order to her being brought to a regular Tryall. . . .

Whereas an Informacion in Behalf of her Magesty was presented by Luk Hill, to the Court in pursuance To Mr Generall Attorneys Tomson report on his Excellency order in Councill the 16th Aprill Last About Grace Sherwood being Suspected of Witchcraft, have thereupon Sworn Severall Evidences against her by which it Doth very likely appear.

June 7, 1706

Whereas at the Last Court an order was past that the Sheriff should Sommons an able Jury of Women to Serch Grace Sherwood on Suspicion of witchcraft, which although the Same was performed by the Sheriff yet they refused And did not appear, it is therefore ordered that the Same persons be againe Sommoned by the Sheriff for their Contempt To be Dealt with according to the uttmost Severity of the Law, and that a new Jury of Women be by him Sommoned To appear next Court to Serch her on the aforesaid Suspicion, and that he likewise Sommon all evidences that he Shall Be informed of as materiall in the Complaint, and that She continue in the Sheriff Costody unless She give good bond And Security for her Appearance at the next Court, and that She be of the Good behaviour towards her Majestie and all her Leidge people in the mean time.

July 5, 1706

Whereas for this Severall Courts the Business between luke hill and Grace Sherwood on Suspicion of witchcraft have Been for Severall things omitted, perticulary for want of a Jury to Serch her, and the Court being Doubtfull That they Should not get one this Court, and being willing to have all means possible tryed either to acquit her or to Give more Strength to the Suspicion that She might be Dealt with as Deserved, therefore it was Ordered that this Day by her own Consent to be tried in the water by Ducking, but the weather being very Rainy and Bad Soe that possibly it might endanger her health, it is therefore ordered that the Sheriff request the Justices precisely to appear on wednessday next by tenn of the Clock at the Court house, and that he Secure the body of the Said Grace till that time to be forth Coming, then to be Dealt with as afore said.

July 10, 1706

Whereas Grace Sherwood being Suspected of witchcraft have a long time waited for a Fit uppertunity For a Further Examinacion, and by her Consent and Approbacion of this Court, it is ordered that the Sheriff take all Such Convenient assistance of boats and men as Shall be by him thought Fitt, to meet at Jonathan Harpers plantacion in order to take the Sd Grace forthwith and put her into the above mans Debth and try her how She Swims Therein, always having Care of her life to preserve her from Drowning, and as Soon as She Comes Out that he request as many Ansient and Knowing women as possible he Cann to Serch her Carefully For all teats spots and marks about her body not usuall on Others, and that as they Find the Same to make report on Oath To the truth thereof to the Court, and further it is ordered that Som women be requested to Shift and Serch her before She goe into the water, that She Carry nothing about her to cause any Further Suspicion. . . .

[Later that day, after the ducking:] Wheras on complaint of Luke hill in behalf of her Majesty that now is against Grace Sherwood for a person Suspected of witchcraft, and having had Sundry Evidences Sworne against her, proving Many Cercumstances to which She could not make any excuse or Little or nothing to say in her own Behalf, only Seemed to Rely on what the Court should Doe, and thereupon consented to be tryed in the Water and Likewise to be Serched againe, which experiments being tryed and She

190

Swiming when therein and bound Contrary To Custom and the Judgment of all Spectators, and afterwards being Serched by Five antient weomen who have all Declared on Oath that She is not like them nor noe Other woman that they knew of, having two things like titts on her private parts of a Black Coller, being Blacker than the Rest of her Body, all which Cercumstance the Court weighing in their Consideracion Doe therefore order that the Sheriff take the Sd Grace Into his Costody and to Commit her body to the Common Goal [jail] of this County there to Secure her by irons, or otherwise there to Remaine till Such time as he Shall be otherwise Directed in order for her coming to the Common Goale of the country [in Williamsburg] to bee brought to a Future Tryall[3] there.

---

1. *What is not mentioned in these proceedings is that, in December 1705, Grace Sherwood brought action against Luke Hill and his wife for assault and battery, claiming £50 of damages and receiving twenty shillings. What this might have to do with Hill's accusation of witchcraft against Sherwood is never brought up in the trial.*

2. *Burr's footnote regarding the move from the county court to the general court (all sic): At this point the court reached the limit of its powers, and Luke Hill, doubtless at its instance, petitioned the highest tribunal of the colony, the General Court, i.e., the Governor and Council, informing them that "one Grace Sherwood of Princess Anne County being suspected of witchcraft upon his complaint to that county court that she had bewitched the petitioner's wife, the court ordered a jury of women to search the said Grace Sherwood who upon search brought in a verdict against the said Grace, but the court not knowing how to proceed to judgment thereon, the petitioner prays that the Attorney Generall may be directed to prosecute the said Grace for the same." But the attorney general, to whom on March 28 the matter was referred, reported on April 16 that he found the charge too general and that the county court ought to have made a fuller examination of the matters of fact, and that "pursuant to the directions and powers to County Courts given by a late act of Assembly" they ought, if they thought there was sufficient cause, to have committed the accused to the general prison of the colony, "whereby it would have come regularly before the Generall Court." Wherefore he suggested "that the said County Court do make a further Enquiry into the matter," and if they find cause for action, to follow the said law; and it was ordered that a copy of his report "be sent to the court of Princess Anne County for their direction in the premises."*

3. *Burr's footnote regarding another trial (all sic): If, at the next session of the General Court, Grace Sherwood came up for trial, the records are missing, and probably perished in the burning of the State Courthouse in 1865. She at least survived the trial; for in 1708 she was confessing judgment for six hundred pounds of tobacco, and in 1733 willing her estate to her three sons. It is not till 1740 that the proving of that will shows her deceased. [NB: A 2006 Washington Post article, however, mentions that she was imprisoned for over seven years, and that verdict is not included in Burr's transcriptions.]*

Featured Writer: Kathryn Smith

2019.

Kathryn Smith is a queer poet and mixed-media artist living in Spokane, Washington. She is the author of two full-length poetry collections: *Self-Portrait with Cephalopod* (Milkweed Editions, 2021), which won the Jake Adam York Prize, and *Book of Exodus* (Scablands Books, 2017). Her poems, embroidery erasures, and visual poetry have appeared in *The Gettysburg Review*, *Permafrost*, *Fugue*, *The Journal*, *Poetry Northwest*, and elsewhere, and she has received awards from the Allied Arts Foundation and Spokane Arts, as well as a Pushcart special mention. Her mixed-media work is often language-driven and includes visual poetry, ink-making, collage, book-binding, and assemblage incorporating elements collected from the natural world (lots of wasp nests and crab shells).

The poems that appear in *Footnote* are part of a chapbook-length series called *Chosen Companions of the Goblin,* which won the Open Country Press chapbook contest in 2018 and was published in 2019. The poems center around the story of the Fox sisters, who became known in the 19th-century American Spiritualist movement for their ability to communicate with the dead.

The story of Maggie and Katie Fox began in 1848, when these sisters (ages 14 and 11, respectively) started communicating with the spirit world. Mediumship quickly became their career. From a young age, these girls became public figures, there for the public to gaze on. People listened to them, but only because other voices—those of the dead—were supposedly speaking through them. Their story, and these poems, are not so much about ghosts as they are about women, agency, societal expectations, feminism, and voice.

The chapbook in which these poems appear combines poetry, erasure poetry, and embroidery art. It considers the social context and scientific advances happening at the same time as the Spiritualist movement. Smith received a Spokane Arts Grant Award for work on this project.

You can learn more about her work at kathrynsmithpoetry.com and by following @paperhermitage on Instagram.

Considering "the Public Appears Disposed to Being Amused Even When They Are Conscious of Being Deceived" (P. T. Barnum, 1855)

Considering the present age of trickery
and the Era of Manifestations,
considering youth and poverty's
boredom, disobedience and its waiting
whip, we followed our sister like lambs.

Considering the evil nature of man,
and woman subsumed by him,
considering the permission a woman
has to speak when the ghost of another
speaks through her, considering everyone
knows that when lambs are led, it's either
to shear or to slaughter. Considering
the suffragists and abolitionists and radical
Quakers, the rattlings against convention,
the Shakers and their visions and egalitarian
God, the angel Moroni and the shroud between
the two worlds fraying. Considering the wolf
will lie down with the lamb. Considering Mesmer
and animal magnetism and mother driven
to madness, how could we then go back.

Considering Brook Farm and Oneida,
the Transcendentalists. Considering electricity
and the telegraph and science explaining the
unexplained. Considering the freedom
of the spirit world, an escape from wrath,
considering grief and its desperation, its
willingness to believe. Considering what balm
attention is for loneliness, the eyes upon you,
the hands upon you, considering the fingers
on the séance table, their gruesome spread
and how they reach for us. Our ankles exposed
to scrutiny, our skirts tied up to the calf.

Considering the spectacle of the fur peeled back,
the shock of a wolf beneath. Considering our
ankles, so furred and lupine, the eyes, the better
to see us with, the eyes of all waiting upon us
and wanting, and why wouldn't we
give them, in this due season, the fruit?

P. T. Barnum,
1851.

Ernestine de Faiber and Phineas T.
Barnum, glass plate collodion negative
by the Mathew Brady Studio, c. 1860-70.

The Fox Sisters
Hold a Séance

To begin, they drape the walls in burgundy cloth,
hide Maggie behind the fabric. She removes
her shoes and flexes her toes. The spirit will send

its message through her body, clicks and raps
in an unnatural series that only her sisters
can translate. At slumber parties, at their age,

I sat on the floor as the other girls
played Light as a Feather, Stiff as a Board,
testing the limits of the metaphysical, pushing against

the resurrection of the body. I didn't believe in the life
everlasting so much as fear what would happen
if I didn't believe. *Do not put the Lord your God*

to the test. Some girls trust instinct enough to conjure
faith from an enterprising trick—though they hid
in shrouded walls and learned to mimic

a ghost at the door, they knew some part of it
was beyond their doing. Young hands will move
the Ouija's pointer by will of an adolescent fervor

that may as well be called supernatural. If the body
lifts, it means it's possible to channel another dimension.
Some things we cannot understand. Before

he married her, Maggie's husband called the sounds
a great mystery: unable to be explained, and yet,
there they were. Even Maggie couldn't decide:

confessing her fakery, then recanting her confession
at the spirit guides' beseeching. Whether each girl's
desire to believe made the body they lifted seem lighter,

or whether a different truth revealed itself
in their incantation, my heart became a tell-tale drum
within me, pounding my chest so hard it shook the floor.

The Fox sisters (left to right: Maggie, Kate, Leah) in a lithograph titled *The Original Mediums of the Mysterious Noises at Rochester Western, N.Y.*, after a daguerreotype by Richard B. Appleby, 1852.

Maggie Fox Speaks to the Dead Girl, Then Is Asked to Remove Her Clothes

When you live above floorboards that hide
fragments of a murdered peddler, it's hard

to leave a room without taking a little
of his spirit with you. I feel it everywhere:

murmuring like song when the church
organ wavers, shuffling my skirts

as I walk through town, blushing my cheeks
on the coldest days. So when Mr. Post

asked what voices would speak to us
outside that house, it wasn't hard

to hear his dead daughter knocking
at another door. The grieved believe what they

need to believe. The spectators maintain
their suspicions. After the message

made itself known in what thumps and clicks
the departed adopt as language,

Mrs. Post ushered us sisters behind a curtain,
where cold-fingered strangers fumbled

our buttons. Dresses dropped with a thud.
We stood exposed, skin flushed

with mystery, bare as Christ before Thomas,
our bodies gaping, holy, like wounds.

The Examination

To prove we are liars the men grasp our knees.
To prove we are honest we allow the men to grasp our knees.
The pressure is applied through the fabric
of the dress. We must consent
to the pressure applied to the knees through the dress,
for the dress is a matter of record.
To prove we are honest we must acknowledge what the dress
might conceal about the female body, what artificial
contrivances might be hidden beneath. We must consent
to examinations repeated and thorough.
To prove we are liars a second doctor places hands
on my feet while the first keeps his hands on the knee.
To prove they are honest, they ask permission.
To prove I am honest, I give permission.
We must acknowledge the dress and the leather of the shoe
are coldly scientific. We must admit to being touched
on every part of the lower extremities to ensure
each part does not produce sound. We must not
produce sound. I consent to examination. They ask
permission, I grant permission. To prove
we are liars the feet are held upon pillows
above any resisting body or any body capable
of resistance. To prove we are honest
we must explain why the spirits refuse to communicate
when the feet rest on cushions and why they won't speak when the hands
of men apply pressure to the knees through the fabric of the dress.
We must explain this. We must explain.

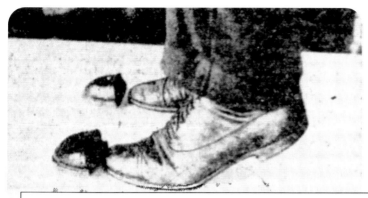

A medium's false shoe tips, made of blackened steel that could be slid over shoes for deception during a séance. According to an article that ran in *The Philadelphia Record* in September 1907: "While the sitter's toes are on those of the medium, the latter has merely to withdraw his own feet, leaving the false tips under those of the sitter." Many séances at the time relied on clicks and noises made by feet under a table.

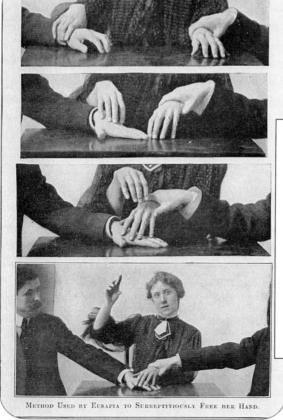

METHOD USED BY EUSAPIA TO SURREPTITIOUSLY FREE HER HAND.

An illustration from a 1907 book that demonstrates how a medium named Eusapia would "surreptitiously free her hand" without her clients knowing. Often, the clients were blindfolded.

Animal Magnetism vs. Spiritual Magnetism, or the Vertiginous Sister Attempts a Mesmeric State in Order to More Fully Understand

I was already
spinning when the man
waved his hands and
commanded trance.
I'm a good girl,
so it's easy
to fall when instructed.
I've always

been good
at being
sickly   I'm jellylegged
I'm clamored   just let me
lie down.
        The Doctor said

it's just an aural
imbalance. Now see

how the demon
        ear will fool you:

aural to aura   auricle   oracle

            an auricular shifting
and see how easily
you
are mistaken.
There's an ear-

shaped pouch
at each atrium of the heart.

It's not my fault   my fall   my falter
            my fall in vertiginous
magnetism.
                I follow
instruction and

I'd been spinning
for days

Everyone
in America was already
spinning

            animals
magnetized
by what they long
to believe, by the heart
that hears
its own skipping,

the ear hears its own spinning

Everyone in America
was already spinning

so I answered the knock
at the door of another
dimension.

Maggie (left) and Kate (right) Fox, 1852.

A "séance at Baron von Erhardt's" on glass negative, photographed by George Grantham Bain, c. between 1898 and 1920s.

An Excerpt from
The History of Spiritualism

Arthur Conan Doyle

First published in 1926 (all sic).

For some years the two younger sisters, Kate and Margaret, gave séances at New York and other places, successfully meeting every test which was applied to them. Horace Greeley, afterwards a candidate for the United States presidency, was, as already shown, deeply interested in them and convinced of their entire honesty. He is said to have furnished the funds by which the younger girl completed her very imperfect education.

During these years of public mediumship, when the girls were all the rage among those who had no conception of the religious significance of this new revelation, and who concerned themselves with it purely in the hope of worldly advantage, the sisters exposed themselves to the enervating influences of promiscuous séances in a way which no earnest Spiritualist could justify. The dangers of such practices were not then so clearly realized as now, nor had it occurred to people that it is unlikely that high spirits would descend to earth in order to advise as to the state of railway stocks or the issue of love affairs. The ignorance was universal, and there was no wise mentor at the elbow of these poor pioneers to point the higher and the safer path. Worst of all, their jaded energies were renewed by the offer of wine at a time when one at least of them was hardly more than a child. It is said that there was some family predisposition towards alcoholism, but even without such a taint their whole procedure and mode of life were rash to the last degree. Against their moral character there has never been a breath of suspicion, but they had taken a road which leads to degeneration of mind and character, though it was many years before the more serious effects were manifest.

Some idea of the pressure upon the Fox girls at this time may be gathered from Mrs. Hardinge Britten's description from her own observation. She talks of "pausing on the first floor to hear poor patient Kate Fox, in the midst of a captious, grumbling crowd of investigators, repeating hour after hour the letters of the alphabet, while the no less poor, patient spirits rapped out names, ages and dates to suit all comers." Can one wonder that the girls, with vitality sapped, the beautiful, watchful influence of the mother removed, and harassed by enemies, succumbed to a gradually increasing temptation in the direction of stimulants?

A remarkably clear light is thrown upon Margaret at this period in that curious booklet, "The Love Letters of Dr. Elisha Kane." It was in 1852 that Dr. Kane, afterwards the famous Arctic explorer, met Margaret Fox, who was a beautiful and attractive girl. To her Kane wrote those love letters which record one of the most curious courtships in literature. Elisha Kane, as his first name might imply, was a man of Puritan extraction, and Puritans, with their belief that the Bible represents the absolutely final word in spiritual inspiration and that they understand what that last word means, are instinctively antagonistic to a new cult which professes to show that new sources and new interpretations are still available.

He was also a doctor of medicine, and the medical profession is at the same time the most noble and the most cynically incredulous in the world. From the first Kane made up his mind that the young girl was involved in fraud, and formed the theory that her elder sister Leah was, for purposes of gain, exploiting the fraud. The fact that Leah shortly afterwards married a wealthy man named Underhill, a Wall Street insurance magnate, does not appear to have modified Kane's views as to her greed for illicit earnings. The doctor formed a close friendship with Margaret, put her under his own aunt for purposes of education whilst he was away in the Arctic, and finally married her under the curious Gretna Green kind of marriage law which seems to have prevailed at the time. Shortly afterwards he died (in 1857), and the widow, now calling herself Mrs. Fox-Kane, forswore all phenomena for a time, and was received into the Roman Catholic Church.

In these letters Kane continually reproaches Margaret with living in deceit and hypocrisy. We have very few of her letters, so that we do not know how far she defended herself. The compiler of the book, though a non-Spiritualist, says: "Poor girl, with her simplicity, ingenuousness and timidity, she could not, had she been so inclined, have practised the slightest deception with any chance of success." This testimony is valuable, as the writer was clearly intimately acquainted with everyone concerned. Kane himself, writing to the younger sister Kate, says: "Take my advice and never talk of the spirits either to friends or strangers. You know that with all my intimacy with Maggie after a whole month's trial I could make nothing of them. Therefore they are a great mystery."

Considering their close relations, and that Margaret clearly gave Kane every demonstration of her powers, it is inconceivable that a trained medical man would have to admit after a month that he could make nothing of it, if it were indeed a mere cracking of a joint. One can find no evidence for fraud in these letters, but one does find ample proof that these two young girls, Margaret and Kate, had not the least idea of the religious implications involved in these powers, or of the grave responsibilities of mediumship, and that they misused their gift in the direction of giving worldly advice, receiving promiscuous sitters, and answering comic or frivolous questions. If in such circumstances both their powers and their character were to deteriorate, it would not surprise any experienced Spiritualist. They deserved no better, though their age and ignorance furnished an excuse. . . .

Photo of Sir Arthur Conan Doyle with Spirit, 1922. The double-exposure of negatives was a pioneering art form used to trick people into believing that spirits could be photographed.

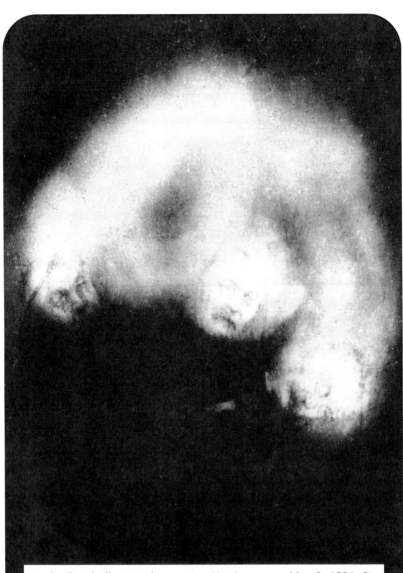

In the Dutch illustrated magazine *Het Leven*, on May 2, 1931, Sir Arthur Conan Doyle's widow claimed in an article that her late husband was still alive and trying to "manifest himself through photographic rays." She posited several photographs taken shortly after his death as proof, each showing the "spirit" of her husband, with the help of a séance conducted by English clergyman Rev. Charles Lakeman Tweedale and photographic medium William Hope. Several of the photos show the spirit of Doyle appearing over the shoulder of his widow and their eldest son, Denis.

William Hope, 1950.

Λ gelatin silver print of the Rev. Charles L. Tweedale and his wife, with the spirit of Mrs. Tweedale's late father, Frank Burnett, looming behind them, taken by William Hope, 1919.

No Locks

Bob Sykora

Nashoba Community, Germantown, Tennessee, 1827.

Fanny Wright says *no locks*, says locks
mean giving up. Last night, Rederick tromped
into Isabel's room, looking for something
that doesn't belong to him. Locks don't talk,

but they do say something. Locks say
we're unsafe. Locks mean hushing behind doors
at the sound of footsteps. Heavy whispers
in the hallway. The buzz of secrets, separation,

some hefty green unfurling in the walls. Rederick
asks about free love, and Fanny's silent eyes
shake the room. *No locks* doesn't mean
you can just have whatever you want. Everyone

drifts to bed, to their unlocked rooms.
Everyone dreams the same dream: an endless
field of metal, locks blooming raucous smiles,
tangling arms, latching and unlatching, laughing

as the green sky dampens and a dark,
impenetrable sea fills the infinity,
and there are no more locks, no more doors,
just a swelling fear that no one is alone anymore.

> Nashoba was imagined as a sort of utopia where enslaved people could "buy" their freedom through labor, mingle with whites, and get educated on the way to freedom in Haiti. It was a misguided community that ultimately failed after 3 years.

At New Lebanon
They Danced like Ghosts

Bob Sykora

Shaker Village, New Lebanon, New York, 1848.

I tried to understand it, all this hooting
and tooting like owls in the woods.
You could hear them two miles out. Tuneless
hymns echoed off the endless meadow *Renounce the World*

for hours. They said they knew I was coming.
They said they'd been waiting. Candles
practiced dying in the window. My feet
practiced falling asleep as they prayed. A quiet

charged with vibrations, oaths, and curses
renting the air. Footsteps somewhere and mouths
spewing groans like the night could escape
through their voices. Shooing and hushing out

evil spirits. Swearing at the devils, the boogers,
the sodomites. And all at once, a veil covered
the night, folding into silence heavier than before.
At supper, I ask: *Do you consider yourself perfect?*

One smiles, answers prompt and quiet: *Yes.*

SHAKERS' DANCE.

19th-century engravings of Shakers engaged in their ceremonial dancing at New Lebanon (also called Mount Lebanon), New York. The Shaker village was founded in 1782. Engravings were made in 1857 (above) and 1870 (below).

SHAKERS.

The Hummingbird Artist Dreams of the Ladder of Heaven

Greg Rappleye

> *Sunday evening, I attended a lecture at The American Union given by the Reverend Fletcher on the Book of Genesis and the works of the English naturalist, Charles Darwin. Spent a fitful night, possessed by strange, recurring dream.*
> —from the notebooks of American painter Martin Johnson Heade in Rio de Janeiro, November 27, 1863

> *He dreamed, and behold a ladder set up on the earth, and the top of it reached to heaven: and behold the angels of God ascending and descending. . . .* —Genesis 28:12

A golden ladder, behold—
a ladder stepped with thirty rungs.
Written on four was *Renounce the World*,
and these were coiled with woody vines,
with anacondas and jeweled snakes.
And laced throughout—hummingbirds—
Ruby Throats and Violet Ears, sipping
At rain lilies and the bluets of the understory.

Above, steps five through seven,
upon which was written *Penitence and Affliction*.
There the Thorntails, raveling along the selvage,
circled the Frilled Coquettes, and drank from gardenias
braided through the golden rungs. And all the air—
redolent of candles, from which a musk-like honey
had never quite been lost.

Rungs numbered eight through seventeen—
a long run of golden steps—inscribed
The Defeat of Vice and Acquisition of Virtue,
by which the birds meant—for in this dream,
he understood their songs—slander, greed, and lust.
Here, Woodnymphs arced with
Sappho Comets, and through the steps
turned passion flowers—their stamens and pistils
despairing—laid open for all to see.

Aroused, he woke and went naked to the veranda.
He looked to the moonlit garden
and the dark of the breadfruit tree, that flowed
like a river, down from the midnight sky.

Called to sleep again, he dreamed steps eighteen
through twenty-six, each of which was honey-gold,
and written there—*The Sins of Loneliness*.
Round these hovered Golden Throats and Sun Gems,
ravening at the sweet of wild indigo.

And he dreamed—was it blasphemy
to dream this?—*If I cannot do what God is doing,
I must steal what God is doing.*

So rose the twenty-seventh, twenty-eighth,
and twenty-ninth steps, upon which was written
Peace of the Soul. There the Streamertails
spiraled among the Plovercrests, and all
of them, male and female, fell upon the columbine
and flame azaleas, while above these, the thirtieth rung—
swaled with clouds, dissolving and re-forming.

And beyond this, *Oh*, a fiery gold,
suffusing the stairway in light.

Passion Flowers and Hummingbirds, a painting by Martin Johnson Heade, c. 1870-83.

Martin Johnson Heade, c. 1870.

Two Hummingbirds with Their Young, an oil painting on canvas by Martin Johnson Heade, c. 1865.

The Notary's Conquest (A Fragment)

Deva Eveland

Being a summary of notable events compiled for His Most Catholic Majesty [King Fernando II] by His humble servant and vassal, Porfirio Beltrán Paniagua, clerk and chronicler of the expedition of 1506, and detailing the acquisition of rich lands for his majesty in the hitherto unknown isle of Augustinia[1].

Several pages following the first are missing. They are thought to have documented the hardships of the sea voyage and the expedition's landing somewhere along the Gulf Coast of present-day Mexico.

[The chief wore a] . . . cotton cloak fastened in the Moorish style with a gold brooch. Though his retinue presented us with venison and thin cakes of yellow meal, he also communicated by signs that he wished us to leave before the next dawn. We feigned disinterest in the food and continued filling our casks from the spring. Captain Agustín wished them to believe us gods nourished only by gold, and so pointed at the cacique's gold brooch and indicated that that was more valuable. The old chief gave it to him. Seeing their leader so docile, Captain Agustín ordered the *Requirimiento* to be read out. As notary I bore witness, and further registered that the elderly cacique agreed to it by signs[2]. Thus on the 1st of October, 1506, he and all his people became vassals of Your Sacred Majesty and acknowledged the Holy Catholic Church as the ruler and superior of the whole world. Captain Agustín next demanded more gold to

---

1. *Paniagua did not seem to understand the expedition had landed on a new continent.*
2. *It is unlikely the cacique had either the linguistic or conceptual framework necessary to understand the Spaniards' intent.*

be brought the following day, and shewed the chief one of the water casks that he might know the quantity of treasure to be delivered. But the chief indicated that he didn't have that much gold; that the land there lacked precious metals. He again made signs that he wished us to leave before dawn. We knew him to be dissembling, though, for the Cuban Indian whom we called Molenque described this as a land of great wealth[3]. As the ancient cacique would not answer any more of our questions, nor reveal the whereabouts of his treasure, Captain Agustín was obliged to set the dogs upon him. The *naturales* were much dismayed to see their lord ripped apart by mastiffs, and fled into the jungle. They are unfamiliar with our war dogs and fear them as monsters[4].

Though we'd finished the last crumbs of cassava bread four days past, Captain Agustín commanded us to await nightfall before partaking of the venison and cakes, as the Indians could have spies hidden in the dense canopy. Were they to see us eating, they would know us mortal. So great was our hunger that the captain put the victuals under armed guard and threatened to hang whosoever disobeyed his orders. Finally, at dusk we secreted ourselves amongst a copse of trees and laid into the provisions like a pack of wild hounds. We all wept in thanks of the divine providence that delivered us from starvation. Fray Echevarria delivered a sermon assuring us that the bounty of sustenance was in reward for having claimed those lands for Christendom.

The contentment in our bellies was tempered, however, by the growing realization that the *naturales* would indeed attack at dawn. All night they beat upon drums and wailed dreadful hymns to Satan. We observed many fires—they easily outnumbered us 1,000 to 1. González and Ibarra argued that we should steal for the brigantines under cover of dark, but Captain Agustín insisted that a retreat would demonstrate weakness before the *naturales*. Had we not read them the *Requirimiento*? Their attack would now constitute an act of rebellion against the Spanish crown and not a defense of

---

3. *The appellation* Molenque *indicates that the slave's teeth were in poor condition.*

4. *The only dog known to the ancient Mesoamericans was the hairless xoloitzcuintli, kept like a small pig for its meat. It was also thought the xoloitzcuintli guided the souls of the dead into the underworld.*

their own territory. As notary, I averred the fact. Legally, it was the same as though the savages meant to lay siege to Toledo itself. Fray Echevarria assured us that so long as we were true to our holy mandate, divine providence would protect us again. From the high torches we deduced that there was a city nearby—perhaps hewn of sheer gold. It is well known that throughout the orient they favor this material over stone. Gold is not only more common, but also softer and easier to work, which delights the Indians as they are much given to idleness. The longer we watched the glow of lights against those faraway battlements, the more clearly we perceived the city to be none other than El Dorado. The men began to tell of how they would spend their share of the spoils, and such talk . . .

More pages are missing here.

. . . till our swords grew heavy with the toil of slaughter. Though the Indians fell before Captain Agustín as the Trojans before Achilles, the jungle there is dense and featureless, and so we could not locate the city, and after a time found ourselves to be whence we had set out from. Succumbing to their timorous nature, the *naturales* began hurling darts at us from places of hiding. They fled as oft we charged. Their inability to match our valor was wearisome, for weighed down by our steel cuirasses in the sweltering heat, we could not engage in melee. Thankfully none of us were slain by this womanly mischief, but all of us suffered injuries and even the mastiffs were wounded[5]. An argument now arose between supporters of Ibarra, who wanted to find a path back to the brigantines, and those who argued for pressing forward to free the seven captured by the Indians[6]. Our surviving peons fled into the jungle, leaving their burden scattered about pell-mell. There was no one to carry the chests of fineries, the casks of water, the cannon and powder, and the records and documents of the expedition—the latter being

---

5. *Paniagua does not count casualties among the Indigenous Cuban slaves, though evidently some were killed.*

6. *The abrupt admission that Spaniards had indeed been captured may point to more missing text. Captain Agustín's conspicuous absence from this debate also hints that he might have been among those taken prisoner.*

my special concern. Having survived the tempests of the Caribbean, I did not intend to see our important papers lost to the lassitude of Cubans. I set out to compel the idiots to resume their obligation to the Crown, that I might rejoin my comrades without abandoning stewardship of our official documents. Though González had been captured, divine providence had at least left his finest war dog, La Condesa to help me track the peons. I resolved to kill a good number of them, lest they come to think it a simple thing to betray the Spanish Crown.

I gave chase best I could, but the devil sent a trickle of sweat into my eyes. With the she-mastiff straining eagerly at her lead, I could not disavail myself of either gauntlet to mop my brow, and thus the bitch pulled me hither and thither through the underbrush. It was beast who claimed dominion over man and not the other way round, for blinded by a stinging veil of perspiration, I could do little except strive to maintain my balance as La Condesa, in her peregrinations, bade me follow her betwixt hanging vines, over clumps of tree roots, and through thickets of brambles. The din of battle grew faint, eclipsed by the shrill drone of the insects that plague those woods.

After a time, it seemed the mastiff had trapped one of the peons. I heard a scrambling across the leaves and felt the jerk of the pull-chain as she pounced. The prey let out a most bestial squeal, revealing itself not to be a Cuban Indian at all. Consumed with her kill, the mastiff ceased to pull at her lead, and I enjoyed a minute's respite to collect my wits and wind. She had slain an enormous hedgehog sprouting ears like a rabbit. For a long time, she fawned over her prize, wagging her tail, whining, and growling as though in solicitation of my favor. When I at last compelled her to resume our mission, she proceeded at a trot, clamping the hare twixt her teeth with greatest pride. We marched till nightfall, unable to locate the expedition, the city of gold, the brigantines, or the escaped peons.

The next day, overcome by a great hunger, I attempted to wrest the hare from the mastiff's jaws, but she would not relinquish it. Indeed, she was pleased by the episode as though it were a game. In desperation, I gathered some vegetables from the forest floor

218

and ate them. Their flesh was green, they were bitter, and I fell sick. Afraid that I could not keep pace with the hound in my weakened state, I lashed the chain fast round my wrist. For many days, she again led me about at her fancy. I was too ill to perceive whither we wandered. Heavy rains increased my misery, though the puddles they left behind kept me from death of thirst. Mosquitoes of three varieties hovered about, so that one species breakfasted upon my flesh, another partook of *la merienda*, and the third a nightly feast. For myself there was no such bounty of foodstuffs. La Condesa once poached an albino worm out of a brook. Though a goliath of its species, it was so heavily masticated by the time she deigned to share it with me that there was precious little meat. Besides, the worm was of such demonic appearance, with horns sprouting out of its gills and oozing sulfurous fumes, I could not, as a Christian, bring myself to eat it[7]. Once she trapped a wild peahen in her great jaws and once a shaggy piglet. On the latter occasion I was in such despair of starvation that I sunk to my knees, sobbing, and begged her in the name of the Imperial Crown to surrender some scrap that I might sup upon. She merely wagged her tail, drooling over the kill beneath her paws. I sternly reminded her that she was descended from none other than *Roldanillo*, but she merely sniffed at the dead creature as though to ignore my beseechings[8]. I lunged, but her spiked collar gave me injury. She again made mischief, bounding away, dragging the limp animal by the nape of its neck and me by the chain round my wrist.

When I'd regained my footing, I lectured her for the rest of the day's march on the seven deadly sins, laying special emphasis on that of gluttony. Evidently my words touched her in some way, for the next morning she dropped a gift on my chest to awaken me. It was a dirt-encrusted hand. At first I was delighted, for it bore a golden ring. Surely the faithful mastiff, guarding her master in his slumber, had slain some Indians preparing an ambush. And as the

---

7. *The animal is possibly an axolotl. Some scholars have further suggested its inclusion is an interpolation, owing to the axolotl's association with the god Xólotl and the underworld in Mesoamerican mythology. (See also footnote 10.)*

8. *"Little Roland," a war dog fabled to have carried the Spanish standard aloft in its teeth to prevent it from falling into Moorish hands.*

index finger was fitted with a most handsome article of jewelry, it seemed that El Dorado must have been nearby. My contentment turned to horror, however, when I examined the ring more carefully and discovered a crest bearing a lion rampant and three-towered castle—it was the hand of Don Agustín! La Condesa led me to a clearing where she had unearthed the extremity, and there I also found the cannon, the powder kegs, and other assorted equipment of our very expedition. We clearly had not retraced our path, though. The land was now rockier, the soil stiffer, and the gnarled trees that grew from it gave off a dry perfume. There was no sign of any Christian save the hand dug up by the mastiff.

Perchance Captain Agustín was still alive, having buried his hand after fending off the attack of a griffin or some such. But why then should he leave the ring? Perhaps he was slain, and the hand was all that was left, so the men had given it a Christian burial. But why then was there no marker? A more terrible thought occurred to me—what if the expedition had been overwhelmed by cannibals, and the hand only saved from their gruesome supper for use in sorcery? After chaining La Condesa to a cannon wheel, I reburied Captain Agustín's hand, erecting a small cross of wood and reciting a prayer to undo any witchcraft. Next I set about inventorying the equipment, for Quartermaster César de Valladolid was among those who perished drinking seawater in our most desperate hour. In the absence of a proper quartermaster, that duty fell upon the notary. Were the expedition to return, they would expect a full account of the provisioning. Most of it was the worse for my absence. The cannon barrel was apart from its chassis, the powder wet, and the expedition documents in gross disorder. I hoped to find a sword (having lost mine in the jungle) but there was none. The large trunk was off its hinges and emptied of all but a few soiled fineries, though its velour covering was not overly torn or stained. One small iron chest remained in perfect condition, and opened easily with a key still hanging from my belt. Inside the box was a fine bolt of brocade. I wept to look upon an unsullied relic of civilization, and to hold its odors to my nose, but from the scattered leaves of parchment I could not reconcile whither the fabric was presented to our expedition by Doña Josefina de León or the

Viceduke of Lombardy[9]. To further complicate my putting the provision back in order, the hand was buried within the circumference of the mastiff's chain, so that she kept pawing about the grave, forcing me to cease my labors to rebuke and throw rocks at her.

Fortunately, I found a nearby tree that produced large apples of a most peculiar variety. The fruit, which is the size of a lamb, is protected by a thorny green shell. Its pallid flesh is most delicious. Pulling several from the lower branches, I drug them back to the encampment. La Condesa took no interest in these apples, merely sniffing at them in disdain. While I was careful not to gloat too considerably, I could not help but relish in our reversal of circumstances—while I had ample victuals, she now went without. As I ate, however, she fixed upon me with a forlorn gaze so piteous that I could take no pleasure in the feast. Her large woebegone eyes compelled me to go in search of a more suitable foodstuff for her. I did not dare unchain her, though, lest her peregrinations once again lead us astray. There was neither bowyery nor shot to conduct a proper hunt, so I stripped off my cuirass with the idea that I could bring it down hard with both hands upon a small animal. Sadly, the land there was bereft of game to be so clubbed. On my return, however, I chanced upon the carcass of a hind scarcely a quarter league from our camp. As I was just dragging it back, I heard a loud roar. At first, I assumed the beast to be a griffin, but in fact I had robbed a spotted lion of her prey. Seeing the beast leap down from its treetop nest, I dropped the doe and took flight. Not content in merely reclaiming its property, it pursued me; I threw myself into the great velour-covered trunk and hid under the mud-caked fineries therein. Peering out over the lip, I realized that the mastiff, still chained to the cannon wheel, would be left to repel the beast's assault unaided.

As the lion is wont to clamp its jaws round the neck of its prey to kill it, La Condesa's spiked collar saved her life. The beast had scarce pounced when it slunk back into the high grasses, mewling most wretchedly. Still, La Condesa suffered long bloody claw marks

---

9. *Ludovico Galeazzo, who was later excommunicated after claiming Christ had returned as an olive tree growing outside his palace.*

up and down her gaunt ribs. She could do aught but pant and whimper. I had little choice but to unlock the small chest and use the unsullied cloth it held to bandage her up with. Hastening to depart those lion-infested lands, I fashioned a sort of chariot for the injured La Condesa to ride in by lashing the large trunk to the undercarriage of the cannon. With her I stashed the documents, the apples, and a little of the powder. No more would fit. I pulled the whole contraption along behind me with the mastiff's pull chain, which was looped securely round one of the handles of the chest (the side of the trunk now being the prow, in order to rest better upon the wheeled armature).

I reckoned that even if the island were the size of Hispaniola, we were at most a week's march from the coast in any direction. Had La Condesa not been leading us in circles, we would have long since apprehended the craven peons. Though I lacked her refined olfactory abilities, yet I possessed some little knowledge about navigation through the observation of heavenly bodies. Is it not fitting that our Creator would endow his celestial realm with signs that would lead the pious in discovery of marvels hidden even to the hound's nose and the eagle's eye? With a chuckle, I reminded La Condesa that the MEN of the expedition were to be furnished with a *quincena* of war dogs, not the other way round. She was too soporific to rebut me. As we marched, the trees grew thinner and the sun more punishing. I followed the course of the sun West till my eyes burned. . . .

There is more missing text here.

. . . visions of the Ascension rivaling the Cathedral of Córdoba, only in colors not known to our earthly plane. I entreated the clouds: Whither had the Cuban Indians fled? As I peered into the billowy recesses, the vapors folded in upon themselves to shew me many things, but our escaped peons were not among them. One cloud took the form of Don Agustín's severed hand, and others played out the hopeless days of our sea voyage. As I gazed upon them—rolling and crashing like waves—the ground I stood upon seemed to seesaw as a ship's deck in a tempest. And so, too, I felt the distemper of a man at sea, and my throat burned as in those grim days we drank seawater. I tried to remind myself that I looked upon the Kingdom of God, yet I perceived nothing Godly. The sun, obscured by vapor, appeared as a disk of black feathers[10]. Perhaps, I wondered aloud, these visions of past folly were instead sent by the Devil to torment me. I turned to La Condesa and bade her to waken, for such hounds are trained to sniff out the brimstone that accompanies demonic appearances. Though I gave her carriage a mighty shaking, the mastiff was sluggish. Her jaws hung apart, allowing the swollen tongue to loll about her brocade wrappings. Her eyes were crusted over with yellow liquid, and I feared she was lost. When I whispered apologies in her folded ear, she would not rouse, but cracked one eyelid and gave me such a sly look I ascertained at once that she was only feigning mortal injury to secure my obedience. Incensed, I threw down the pull chain. Why should I humble myself like some Arabian slave, carting her about on a litter? Honor obliged me to continue alone. As I staggered forward, there was naught but a vast expanse of desolation. The stunted, prickly weeds filled me with melancholy. And so again I thrust my eyes heavenward to navigate by the clouds, though if their council was angelic or hellborn I knew not. The horizon was ringed with misty apparitions of all the wonders of the isle (which in that moment I christened Augustinia): Above the distant hills I witnessed in swirling vapor the armies of Gog and Magog, and so I knew below those clouds must lie the valley where Alexander the Great imprisoned them so long ago. The lofty spires of El Dorado loomed up from another cloud stretching behind me (as was proper, for that was the direction we had come from). To what I deemed the East was one formed like a pygmy with long ears that he wrapped about his body in lieu of clothing. Floating beside the diminutive savage, a one-breasted Amazon. I surmised that both races must live to the East, locked in a state of perpetual war. In the western skies, dog-headed Cynocephali danced round the Fountain of Youth with such gaiety that I broke into a fit of laughter that tore at my throat like

---

10. *This sentence is clearly an interpolation; it refers to the black sun of the underworld, which the dog-headed god Xólotl bore on his back.*

aguardiente[11]. An apparition of La Condesa arose from the center of the pool, healed of her injuries. It was really she the savages were dancing around! I knew I must go back for her. Together we would wash away the day she was maimed, and all the cruel days after. We would capture those curative waters in the name of Your Majesty. For her part, La Condesa would enchant the dog-headed men with her regal bearing. The sight of a high bred Spanish mastiff swaddled in brocade and born about as though on a royal litter would compel them to acknowledge her as their natural superior. I would explain that we were ambassadors of a great cacique from across the oceans. The Cynocephali would beg me (through whines and yips) to tell them more of our lord Christ that their souls might be saved, and in return I'd form them into a great Christian army to march upon the mosques of El Dorado. I ran back a full league to explain all of this to La Condesa, but she did not so much as twitch an ear. Judging by the foul air her wounds emitted, I knew I must make haste. With trembling gauntlet, I produced the *Requirimiento* from the large trunk and read it out before the clouds, bearing witness to the fact that I had done so in my capacity as a notary. To Your Sacred Majesty I . . .

Man with a dog head from *The Nuremberg Chronicle*, an illustrated encyclopedia by Hartmann Schedel and Michael Wolgemut, 1493.

11. *The earliest surviving transcription of* The Notary's Chronicle *describes the Cynocephali as wearing* máscaras de perro *(dog masks). However, it would make little sense for dog-headed humans also to be dog-masked. The error may be due to a transcriber conflating dog-headed mythological creatures of European origin with New World priests who wore masks of Xólotl during certain rituals relating to the soul's journey after death.*

The Tribe of Men

Daryl Scroggins

I t was the boy who found the sword. His face shone as he brought it in, holding it as he would present a board lined with yams he had dug himself. But he appeared worried that the range of his adventures would be discovered.

"Where did you get that?" his mother asked, looking up from the clay vessel where the day's bread was baking.

"In some bones," he said, still smiling.

"Did these bones have clothes?" she asked.

"No, I swept dust away, and there it was."

She took it from him. Tilted it in two hands so its surface, still bright in places, threatened to show some other sky. "Take it back," she said. "And don't tell your father about this."

"But it could be sold," the boy said.

"Yes," his mother said. "To people who might come back with it, just like the bones did."

Later the woman looked up from the bowls she was filling with soup, and saw her husband, out in front of the hut, slashing at his future with a long, bright blade. Still a boy, really. The goats watching with their tired horizontal eyes.

Beginnings Emerge Out of Endings and the Like

D. Seth Horton

G eorge may or may not have also been in step with it all: the planks of wood, the sickness, the salt within the water. After navigating past the rocks and rockheads of the Chesapeake Bay, his meals were spent mostly on dolphin and barracuda. He saw the sea and tasted it, too. At nineteen, fatigue wasn't going to fell the young man down.

Tuberculosis had forced his older brother into something of a different sort. Since boarding *The Success*, Lawrence had coughed about from bow to stern in a sweat-clogged circularity. He noted with precision that lungs are the weakest of all organs, animal or otherwise. Heaven was going to get itself tracked along—give him another ten months, max—but on this day there was blood. There was sputum. And then, suddenly, there was Barbados.

Wow—the island looked to be fluorescent green and floating. Lawrence thrust out an index finger smeared with snot and said, "Ahoy." He hoped that the healthy air wouldn't be just another final notice.

Here's how it was in point of fact, not in fiction. George helped his brother disembark as if already believing in himself. Maturity grows out of the moment by moment. They walked far enough to behold that Bridgetown held onto its bigness, and in a day or two, they settled all the way through the city.

One hot afternoon by chance, Lawrence grabbed himself onto the opposite side of a bed and groaned accordingly. "Remember?" he whispered. Back when they were boys, someone they knew—a parent perhaps, or whoever—used to say, "Everything alive will soon eat or be eaten."

"I know what you're after," George said with exactly the grace that was required, given the circumstances. He was learning how to smooth over situations involving a life-and-death ilk. "But shouldn't we admit that pendulums rarely swing beyond their targets?"

"Hoo-hah," Lawrence said. Those colonial chops of his slackened out the English as best they could. The ooey-gooeyness of his tone implied that he'd somehow lumbered himself into a porous kind of position.

Brothers help brothers in times of great wanting it. George got around to the basic idea and then agreed to get some doctors who specialized in the science of miracles. After examining Lawrence, one of these men packed his mouth with pearls and said, "The best way to live is to have something that other people want." The other doctors mimed across themselves in agreement. From their learned perspective, the circumference of one's soul should be half the length of one's eventual corpse.

Pragmatic in both the heart and bone, George slinked away to his bedroom. The terrors of the coming war would prove even harder to ride inside and out. By that time, though, Lawrence's death would have given him the guts to advance headlong all the way into independence.

That's a story for another story.

For now, on this particular night in the Caribbean, the future president fed his brother a jellied consommé. He sponged away the cold sweat and blanketed him down into bed. And if he also began to fear that his world was separating altogether around him, well, that's because it most certainly was.

Lawrence Washington was the older half-brother of George Washington. Lawrence, shown here in an engraving c. 1738, would not recover from tuberculosis in Barbados and would die back in Mount Vernon a year later, 1752.

The Smoker's Lot

Gareth Hipwell

Though gold had lately been removed from the diggings in such quantity that a man might have expected the very rotation of the Earth to be affected, however minutely, by the displacement of mass northward, the world wheeled on, and autumn deepened. Frost and fog closed about the field, tempering the soil of Gibson's Plain and the wending reaches of its river to the hardness of cold steel. Water froze in dam and cradle; blue slate cracked and cleaved upon the hillsides, while man, horse, and bullock alike commended gusts of white impermanence to the voidlike cold. Of those vapors expelled from the mouths of men, no small portion consisted in the smoke of tobacco of all cuts and colors. Yet few miners remaining on the Snowy River exhaled that substance in such volume as Francis Keene, one-time woolshed clerk of Sydney.

A chum of good standing on the diggings with a penitent's taste for the work of the prospector, Keene now sat most days on a low wooden bench beside his hut, quietly cursing the want of commerciality that was, he felt, the very worst of Jack Frost's native failings. Keene's hands—so often engaged in the business of filling and setting a light to his filthy kaolin pipe—were heavily callused, the nails split by countless hours spent at work in and on the earth. By contrast, the hands of his partner on the field, one Master Joseph Taylor of Goulburn, were soft as a miser's purse and near as fine besides. For Keene, work and smoke both had been undying sources of satisfaction here above the snowline. Now, though, the icebound soil of the Keene-Taylor claim was frozen solid, impervious to shovel and mattock alike. The two men had fallen necessarily to indolence. Taylor, being possessed of uncommon foresight, had decided against trying to work the winter ground before ever the first frost had settled on the plain.

For all the privations of the season, there came yet new arrivals to the Kiandra goldfield this late autumn 1860. Leg by leg, the spiders felt their way up damp gullies and through chill passes from the southern goldfields. Along the mountain roads they came, in loose formation, with tools and provisions slung across their backs. Their caravans were wreathed in an acrid blue vapor—it being the documented habit of the creatures constantly to smoke a peculiar blend of sundried native plants. This smoke, it was said, kept the spiders' carapaces clear of pests and parasites. The toxicology of the drug, though, was rumored to heighten the pitch of Johnny Black Crab's already vile disposition. Yet, as though in defiance of the primeval appearance and fearful reputation of their species, several individual spiders carried upon their vast thoraxes tokens of an all-too-human civilization. They brought with them lumber and weatherboard by the square acre, nails, currency, shovels, canvas, and even the several working parts of a heavy German letterpress.

As filthy gray clouds brought the first of many heavy snowstorms to bear on the goldfield, Joseph Taylor scooted across the frozen mud and icebound puddles of what passed for a street at the edge of the camp. Teeth on edge, he bounded into the squat slab hut he shared with Francis Keene, bearing a newspaper beneath his muddied coat. The text of the broadsheet clung to the page at a seasick angle befitting the crude township that had given this first run of the *Kiandra Pioneer* both name and circulation. Taylor carried also such quantity of Barrett's Twist as he had today been able to procure.

"There are talks afoot at Kidd's for the establishment of a hospital," Taylor announced. "A vacant lot off Broadway is offered for the purpose." A small flurry of snowflakes licked at his bootheel as he closed the door against the day behind him.

"What good it will do us now," Keene remarked.

The bowl of Keene's pipe was gone cold, emptied of all but a greasy layer of soot. He had not had his smoke in almost three hours. Such was Keene's appetite for tobacco that he could no longer tell the difference between the noxious smoke of a cheap, Mephistophelian plug and the pure, gossamer vapors of a fine Virginia flake. It was the brute act of smoking alone that so forcefully directed the young prospector's cravings. In this pursuit he was a man of rare genius. Keene had a special talent for keeping a fill alight in all weathers, and frequently obtained more than an hour's enjoyment from a single bowl.

"Though I hate to tell you your business," Taylor had once needled his partner beneath markedly clearer alpine skies, "you might find you had a better eye for the color if you removed your face from behind that veil of smoke. If only the once!"

"But that would defeat the purpose of my being here," Keene had replied to the barb. "I gave away the woolshed that I might have my smoke and my work at the same time."

Taylor placed the newspaper on a stool and removed his tin of fresh tobacco from an inside coat pocket. The youthful Taylor had always taken it for a necessary incident of equal partnership that Peter's tobacco was likewise Paul's to enjoy. As to the inverse proposition, Keene had yet to test his partner's convictions.

"Might I—?" Keene croaked.

Taylor looked up with a sharp jerk of his head. "Beg pardon?" he asked. "The—of course." By a slow movement, Taylor offered up a portion of his new-bought twist.

Keene stoked his pipe with deft precision and struck a light. "Tell me," he began through a sudden cloud of smoke, "did you encounter Johnny Black Crab abroad this morning?"

"I did not. Though talk is that certain of the headmen among the spiders have been reconnoitering for claims at the Nine-Mile with, as I heard it put, *no small measure of tenacity.*"

"We shall have clear warning if they come looking for claims closer to the camp," Keene observed. "Lord knows we will smell them long before we see them in the flesh."

Taylor bunched his beard in a cold fist. "The reek of death," he said.

Keene groaned and rolled over onto his back. He considered the condensation that clung to the canvas ceiling above his cot. Taylor, meanwhile, made to stew a joint of bacon on the blackened range of native stone at the near end of the hut. He chewed on a wedge of cheese and waited for the pot to boil. Cheese and bacon both were pregnant with the smoke of cheap tobacco.

Joseph Taylor, not twenty-two years old, had spent his first month on the Snowy River diggings possessed of neither claim nor industry. Francis Keene, by contrast, had been among the first of the chums to arrive on the newly proclaimed goldfield and (weather permitting) had spent every day here since his first hard at work upon the neatly staked riverbank claim that was his worldly lot. Taylor, though a beggar without rags as far as title to a working claim was concerned, had mulishly refused to take up payable new ground any distance from the encampment. He shuddered even now to think of the men on the outlying Five- and Nine-Mile diggings. Taylor despised the ubiquitous balled tussocks of the plains —their wiry foliage an indeterminate gray-green—and reviled the thickets of stunted eucalypts that broke in long, shallow-rooted waves over the surrounding hillsides. Even the camp, with its sloping roofs—the surest indication, when viewed from a distance, that human hands have been at work upon a landscape, for nature will frequently produce a square edge but almost never a triangle— seemed to Taylor an uncanny growth. While the warm chimneys of Kiandra proper gave the impression of security and comfort, Taylor felt it keenly that the nascent township offered only an illusory promise of safety. It was then well known, and much lamented, that a magistrates' court had yet to be declared.

Upon first encountering Francis Keene in the breakfast-arrayed dining room of Reilly's Inn, Taylor had been struck at once by the soil trapped beneath the overhang of Keene's fingernails. Within the space of three or four meetings, the two men had struck up a serviceable rapport. Though a small opening, Taylor found in it room enough to employ his modest talent for wheedling.

"I am burning through my capital in bed and board faster than seems fair," he had remarked at breakfast one morning. "The food here is dear by any scale, and to judge from the noise of the street, I will soon be murdered in my bed into the bargain. I do not expect the advance I have put down for my lodging will stretch to cover the cost of embalming fluid, coffin nails, and a casket, either."

"We might simply leave you in the river for the duration of the colder months, moored to a stake," Keene had quipped. "Come springtime, you would thaw out very nicely on a sunny bank. By then, perhaps, you may be better placed to afford your burial?"

"Should there be any such shortfall, the hotelier had better not look to my father for reimbursement of the additional outlay."

By this blackhearted exchange, Keene had unwittingly sealed for himself an impecunious union. While he was loath to carve up his tiny empire and to divide his energies between working the washdirt of his claim on the one hand and negotiating the exigencies of partnership with Taylor on the other, it was Francis Keene's peculiar habit to offer up things he was either unable or unwilling to give in order to avoid the embarrassment of his friends.

"I could hardly have you pay for a month's bed and board only to see you leave the camp in a box, I suppose," Keene had offered with a leery smile.

"Very Christian of you."

"Perhaps," Keene continued—the words dragging his throat and tongue with hook claws even as they were expelled—"perhaps, given the likelihood you will not now secure a surface claim close to camp at a reasonable price, you might consider going in with me?"

Vain hope has its clearest expression in agonized silence. Then, "You're quite sure, Keene?"

"Sure? No. Tired of offering you unpaid counsel, undeniably."

"I have twisted your arm, then?"

"You have. Though you did well to catch it—I have hardly ceased to dig and pan and rock a cradle these weeks, and would probably be so occupied now, but that you are resolved to plague me."

In this way, Joseph Taylor had wedded himself to the pragmatic Keene's own spirit of possibility and enterprise. But it is axiomatic on the goldfield that the miner—whether partnered or otherwise—cannot hope to realize the possibility that is his claim without first committing to the application of industry. Until a man knows properly the feel of the tools and the tenor of the work, he will know only excitement and enthusiasm for the job at hand. But any hope of finding lasting satisfaction in the business of prospecting is false and reedy. It is all vacancy; the thrill of expectation a prelude to weariness, boredom, and frustration. For six days, Joseph Taylor bent his shoulders over the cradle and knew naught but dewy excitement in its every ebb and flow. But on the seventh day, he was struck with a brutal realization.

"My chest, Keene, is heavier by the hour. To breathe is agony."

"You ought feel free to take a draught from my canteen, there," Keene had replied, gesturing at the battered flask deposited on the riverbank.

"Even rum, I feel, will not keep the chill off this afternoon."

"I hadn't seen you take any."

"No. I wonder that you see anything from behind your smoke."

"Do you mean to break early?"

"My partner permitting."

"I permit it. Will you go to Kidd's, then, or to the Union?"

"My lodgings are yet at Kidd's."

"Yes." Keene, bent-backed, had paused to consider his partner. "Will you take the week's find to be weighed?"

"I should be glad to—though I know nothing of the procedure."

Slurry ran free from Keene's cradle in volume, the admixture disappearing into a bed of wet gravel.

Drawing a labored breath, Taylor had tasted disappointment on the lazy breeze. Where was the huge nugget he had lately felt so certain of finding? A week prior he had been secure in the knowledge that such a treasure would surface from the dirt before ever the first blister arose on his palm. Yet here he stood, blisters stinging feet and hands both, and a cold mountain wind gnawing at his knuckles. There was cold comfort to be found here in pocket or pan.

Whether or not the reek of weed-smoke heralded their arrival in Kiandra proper, the mining classes among the spiders were upon the camp within a fortnight. Heavily tooled teams ventured in from the outlying diggings, and set at once to working the hard winter earth. Who owned, by right, the vacant lots selected by the spiders for working, no one professed to know. Mr. Andersen, a neighbor of the Keene-Taylor enterprise, reported hearing it in The Union that an outfit comprising Messrs. Hart, Pilgrim, and Bishop had sold its own sizeable claim to a spider syndicate for a tolerable, if not strictly reasonable, price. The spiders had been mild and fair in their dealings with the men, it was said, though Hart and his partners had since left the Snowy River and so could not be called upon to confirm the reports. Still, for the isolated men who remained on the lead, it seemed incontrovertible that Johnny Black Crab now worked the half-pinched claims of miners then absent from the diggings.

July unraveled, and the ground solidly refused to surrender its auriferous bounty to human hands. Funds, accordingly, ran short among the miners. This was itself no great problem since supplies were likewise depleted in such stores as remained open for trade. The attendant malaise was Protestant in tone. Tobacco grew especially scarce. Keene, being possessed of wisdom enough to see that a little smoke each day was preferable to smoke in plenty for a week followed by a week of abstinence, took to rationing the small stockpile of foul plug he had managed to accumulate. If it did not see him through the worst of the winter, he reckoned, it would come close. In so reckoning, though, Keene did not factor upon Joseph Taylor.

"I wonder if I might beg a fill, Keene?" the younger man asked one painfully clear alpine afternoon. "My twist, as you might imagine, does not burn half as long as that foul incense you yourself prefer—especially at this altitude."

Keene stretched the fingers of each hand atop the blanket of his cot. He rued that his natural inclination toward generosity and goodwill had, like his partner, been sealed up with him in this hovel. "I can spare a very small portion this morning," he answered. "But we must resupply as soon as one of the storemen secures stock."

"Of course, Keene."

In the impossible brightness of the day outside, the spiders were already hard at work along the length of the river. To count the plumes of blue-gray smoke that rose now from their claims gave as good an indication as any of their total number on the field. Keene stood for a time by the narrow window of the hut and watched them. Though the eight legs of a crab at first suggested confusion, he thought, to study one at work offered a unique lesson in precision. With the hooked feet of its frontmost limbs, the spider miner would cut out neat squares of snow and ice, which it would then peel away from the earth, exposing a workable portion beneath. By some mysterious and oddly genitive chemical process, the creatures were able to liquefy the frozen soil, scooping it up in great armfuls—four front legs pressed together two-by-two being uniquely suited to the task—and depositing it into their cradles. Keene was struck by the almost mechanical locomotion of the individual spider. Black, pistonlike legs rose and fell in time, while individuals on friendly terms opened and closed the fleshy polyps that most men took for mouths in greeting or idle chatter. The vast clouds of exhaustlike smoke that gave out from the creatures' lungs only added to the illusion of their mechanization. It was as though the spider were an engine uniquely adapted to the task of mining the color.

"I've just had it from Booth," Taylor reported as he filled his pipe, "that a gang of spiders has sealed up a lone digger, alive, in the shaft of the Hastings Mine."

Taylor was newly returned from Reilly's Inn. The gossip of the drinkers holed-up there during the day—and in the camp's other public bars besides—was now the only source of news to be had this side of Tumbarumba. Acres of mocking snow had brought real isolation to the camp. The operations of the *Pioneer* had been shelved for some weeks.

"On the Five-Mile?" Keene asked.

"Or very near it."

"No. I cannot credit it that anyone now remains on the Five-Mile. What does Mr. Commissioner Cloete say?"

"Certainly no one on two legs," Taylor snapped. "And the winter may have further horrors in store for us yet. There stand, after all, only a sheet of canvas and a half-inch thickness of board between us and half the crabs of the colony."

Keene clenched his jaw tightly around the mouthpiece of his pipe. "Were the spiders minded to attack us," he said, "we would not be safe on Pinchgut—yet here we are, still drawing breath."

The following morning, while Keene lay sleeping in his cot, Taylor raided the older man's tobacco tins and removed most of the plug they contained. Finding the hut a little cramped, he absented himself shortly thereafter and spent near to three days drinking and smoking in the public bar of the Kiandra Hotel. On the morning of the third day, having staggered out onto the hotel's porch to survey the township, Taylor looked up to see a spider standing out against a sky of dishwater gray atop the slope of New Chum Hill. It had ceased in the relentless activity that was, as much as a column of blue smoke, talismanic of its species. The spider stared at the inebriated man with fixed curiosity. Taylor, unnerved, averted his eyes and fiddled instead with a fill and a light.

Meanwhile, on the far side of the camp, Keene struggled to shake the night's rest from his weary eyes. Late the night before, upon checking his stockpiled plug for signs of damp and spoil, he had been dismayed to find the contents of his three remaining tins substantially scooped out. Today—his native pragmatism being undisturbed by the anger that now boiled inside him—Keene had resolved to defer the tongue-lashing he intended for his partner and to replenish his now tiny reserve of smoke, at any price. But several things had happened to thwart Francis Keene before ever he rose from the cot. Of the Kiandra storekeepers yet in business, one lay prone with fever, while another had taken advantage of back-to-back clear days and ventured on horseback to Lambing Flat—on business unknown to all but himself. The only fellow now trading, a Mr. Wright, had no tobacco to sell at all ("not even a portion of spilled flake swept up from the floor? not a rank wad spoiled by moisture, or once-chewed?"). The scouring rigors of the winter economy having retarded the tides of commerce at Twofold Bay, Dixson & Sons Tobacconists had lately failed in its enterprise there, and no dray had succeeded in making it over the mountains from Tumut, or south from Goulburn, in more than a fortnight.

"If only a man could smoke the snow and eat the mud, this would be Arcadia in the South," Wright quipped as Keene departed the store, slope-shouldered.

Outside of an equal partnership, it was an unspoken tenet on the diggings that a man must never beg a smoke from a fellow addict. This notwithstanding, Keene tried his luck at the bar of Kidd's Exchange Hotel—his only concern being that he conserve the small stock of smoke now remaining to him for as long as possible. Happily, Keene found that a measure of charity yet inhered in several of the chums stationed there, and he spent a more pleasant afternoon than he had anticipated in their company—notwithstanding the tenor of the barroom conversation, which centered, often heatedly, upon the so-called "land question" then inflaming Parliament.

Returning to the hut in the salmon light of the late afternoon, Keene discovered a sour-smelling Taylor fast asleep, lying face down, in a soiled shirt and trousers. A quick inspection of the drunk's coat pockets confirmed that which Keene already feared: nothing remained of his missing plug. Outside, the bright, clear sound of the spiders' implements striking quartz and slate rang out across the clearing.

Ever, as we have seen, a man of singular tendencies, it was Francis Keene's habit to punish those who had wronged him with inexplicable acts of kindness. Seeing in his every fellow—rightly or wrongly—his own good nature mirrored, Keene held it always that the guilty conscience must, when confronted with its smiling victim, contort and writhe in suffering like a snake thrown on the coals of a cooking fire. Yet there was perversity at play here, too. For Francis Keene—in most other respects an entirely worthy soul—actually delighted in the sensation of having been wronged. It was his pleasure to savor a thrill of righteous rage—to twist the barb, ever deeper, into his own flesh. All of this is to say that, when Taylor awoke the following morning—head sore, whiskers reeking of sour milk—Keene reached immediately for the last of his tobacco and wordlessly offered his disheveled partner a smoke. Though the thieving ingrate accepted the proffered token with a grateful nod, yet Keene sensed a wary hesitation in Taylor's movements. Not a word passed between the two bunkmates until well past midday. This standoff was all the more damaging to Keene's rationing effort, since want of conversation is apt to bring on uninterrupted bouts of nervous smoking. So it came about that within the space of three short days, the partners had not a fill left between them.

Keene, prone, spent a day's rest fuming in the close cold of the hut. He grew more irritated by the hour. The older man's mood was made ever darker by the incessant twitching of Taylor's booted feet, and the snatches of dance tunes the other man hummed from time to time without ever striving to resolve a single piece. Above all else, Keene was irritated by Taylor's silent though resolute refusal to go out into the camp and to inquire of Mr. Wright when he next expected a consignment of stock. Keene noticed for the first time the heavy scents of the hut: damp calico, stale leather, bacon tallow. The ubiquity and clinging quality of such odors further inflamed Keene's temper, until he felt it vital that he take himself for a walk.

Outside, a miserable winter afternoon lay in ambush, though it was a clear day, and sunny. Keene brought the heel of his boot down sharply upon an icebound puddle and cursed that it should refuse to crack. He spat onto the surface of the ice in frustration. His spittle was clear, and very frothy.

"I have nothing for you today, I'm afraid," Wright confessed from behind his well-scrubbed counter. "Any day now, I hope, but nothing today."

"Should Mr. Taylor—Joseph, my partner, whom I believe you know to look at—should he find you with a quantity of twist or plug in stock at any time, please advise him that you are instructed to jot up any such purchase of his to my account."

"I do, and I will."

"Thank you," said the unhappy Keene.

It was, by this time, the somewhat notorious habit of the very coarsest souls in the camp to hole-up in a hut or hovel for days at a stretch, there to smoke the putrid herb so favored by Johnny Black Crab. Keene himself had heard more than one miner confess to having tried the drug with substantially enjoyable results.

"Absent tobacco," a wizened chum had once told him, "the crabs' smoke is the best a man can do for himself on the plain."

Of course, reports and confessions such as these were neither the worst nor the strangest species of tale to be savored in the dozen or more hotels of Kiandra and the district. Almost from the very hour of their arrival on the lead, the spiders had attracted rumors of unnatural prostitution. By far the most notorious story in this vein was that of one Matthew Holt, being putatively a miner of flesh and blood now conspicuous in his absence from the diggings. A chum of remarkably small stature—he wore, it was said, the boots of a child—and over-fond of rum, to whit, Holt had reportedly found himself spurned one evening by those battlers then known to him on the field (the molls being uncommonly busy as a result of the heavy rain then fouling up the claims). Being then at the crest of a most lustful fervor, the desperate man was alleged to have sought out a spider procurer. Tellers of the tale milked for gales of laughter the image of the poor, drunken, diminutive Holt struggling to reach his goal with his modest tackle. Eventually, so the story went, the unfortunate and degenerate man—who was, it seems, far from deterred by his pains, though many a worser man would surely have taken them for the intercession of nature itself—called out for a stool.

"But where did he *put it?*" the greener of the chums among the audience would inevitably ask. Not one man in a hundred would offer clarification on that score, of course, though a substantially greater number were undoubtedly in possession of detailed insight.

Much like the hapless Holt, Keene was driven now to distraction by a craving it seemed he might never slake. He began instinctively to finger the pipe in his inside coat pocket. The implement was caked to the core with a black, creosotelike coke that gave out an oily scent even through the close weaves of gabardine and wool. Keeping to the leeside of New Chum Hill, Keene made his way boldly along the edge of the spiders' stopes, drives, and runs, heading determinedly toward what had long been taken for the crab camp on the edge of the bush. Only the occasional spider foreman glanced at Keene as the incongruous human prospector picked his way across the claims. The spiders worked on, liberating gold from the lead at a rate their human counterparts could only imagine.

As though in further demonstration of the species' commitment to efficiency, the spiders' camp was confined to the wooded area beyond the diggings. Not an inch of workable ground, Keene noted, had been given over to convenience or comfort. The creatures' shelters were formed of calico sheets stretched tight over grass-lined pits. These dwellings were themselves grouped tightly together with a spider's economy. Here was a creature content to live one atop the other in swarm- or nestlike fashion. On the outskirts of the encampment, graying bones had been heaped against the trunk of a substantial eucalypt. Keene felt a cold bolus—an admixture of fear and withdrawal—condense in the pit of his stomach. His longjohns clung to his abdomen and thighs. With a wary sigh, he crossed the alpine treeline, stepping into the chill, damp world beyond.

Young spiders darted into nests and hollows as Keene pressed deeper into their midst. Their presence was betrayed to the hapless miner's dulled senses by little more than the suggestion of movement, the muted sound of scampering, and the faintest glint of a carapace or limb. Of adult crabs, Keene saw not a single one. Taking a careless step, he planted his foot in a shallow sphagnum bog. He sensed a strange movement in the moss and mud that had swallowed his extremity, and glanced downward. A choir of tiny yellow frogs, their backs pocked with raised black markings the shape and texture of plague sores, swarmed about his ankle. He pressed on.

Before a clearing at the far side of the spider settlement, Keene happened upon a crude *gunyah* of hessian, bark, earth, and iron. Beside the structure there grew a stout gum, into the flesh of which had been carved the ragged letters *T-R-A-D-E*. The deep gouging by which the word had been formed spoke to a hooked tool wielded with considerable force. Keene approached the lean-to with a nervous frown. He smelled the faintest ghost of an alien smoke. The proprietor of the store emerged from among a nearby stand of twisted snowgums. He—for Keene took the spider merchant for a male of its species—sputtered a greeting in a series of staccato noises no man could hope to replicate. The crab wore a tattered strip of coarse red cloth tied like a scarf around a hind leg. It smoked a spindly tin pipe and raked at the ground with clawed feet.

"I am here to buy *weed*," Keene said. "What is the price?"

The crab retrieved a tattered sheet of ledger paper from some dark recess beneath its thorax and held it out for Keene's inspection. Keene lifted it to his face to read. It was warm and greasy, and redolent of termites. A stock-list. The spider kept up its weird vibrato as Keene retrieved four shillings from his coat and received in return an old flour sack half-filled with green, resinous plant matter the consistency of coarse sugar.

"Thank you," Keene said.

"*Wekkome*," rasped the spider merchant.

From the corner of his eye, Keene watched as a decrepit old crab with half a leg missing twisted apart the limp carcass of a wallaby, shucking meat and gristle from ruptured joints with its terrible mandibles. Keene filled the bowl of his pipe as he walked, set a match, and was immediately enshrouded by a roiling blue cloud.

As the imperious mountain wind sought in vain for human chests to inflame, the afternoon drew out heavy and gray across Gibson's Plain. Tussocks poked from beneath the receding snow-cover. A nagging curtain of rain and drizzle had just then ceased to spiral down onto the camp. Despite the thaw, the diggers who had abandoned the field in streams at the onset of winter showed as yet no sign of returning to Kiandra. Even the spiders had begun, very slowly, to work out their claims and move on to new finds across the range. Several, though, remained. Nothing had come of the camp's proposed hospital, and there had not been a newspaper printed in town in almost a month. Those miners who lingered on the field labored, for the most part, beneath New Chum Hill, working tunnels and shafts that had been driven considerably deeper into the lead by the pains of a spider gang. The camp had its laggards and wastrels, too.

Francis Keene woke from a nap he had not meant to take with a dry mouth and a nagging pressure behind his forehead for which there was no accounting. A fog the color of a mallard egg hung before his eyes. He reached instinctively for his pipe and planted it between his teeth. As the dim interior of the hut resolved itself to him, he spied the bent back of his partner at the far end of the room. Keene rose silently from his cot and crept up behind the younger man. Taylor was tipping a quantity of grainy green herb into an empty plug tin.

"What remains of your original capital, Joseph—if I may ask?" Keene inquired of the furtive Taylor.

Taylor, startled, pivoted on the balls of his feet and sought in vain to conceal his stealthy work. "Why should that interest you now, Keene?"

Keene removed the pipe from his mouth momentarily and spat a sticky web of gray-green mucous onto the packed earth floor of the hut. "Where the plot will, I believe, come free, I expect the price of embalming fluid to be somewhat inflated in town."

"You ought not look to my father," Taylor said with an implacable grin.

Outside on the lead, Johnny Black Crab paused in his labors. A dozen or so spiders—a sizeable portion of the creatures then at work upon the field—felt their way slowly over stope and drive, tailing and scree, drawn along as though by minute threads toward a squat little hut on the edge of the camp. The more curious among the spiders gathered just beyond the threshold of the shelter, peering in through gaps in the canvas lining as a digger with a dirty kaolin pipe between his lips raised an elbow high above his shoulder and brought his split knuckles to bear upon the face of his bunkmate again and again and again.

The remains of the 1850s general store in the abandoned mining town of Kiandra, New South Wales, Australia, as photographed in October 2007.

Author Biographies

ENEIDA P. ALCALDE's writing has appeared or is forthcoming in literary outlets such as *Pirene's Fountain*, *The McNeese Review*, *Huizache*, and *The SFWP Quarterly*. She graduated with an MA in creative writing and literature from Harvard Extension School and is a board member for *Oyster River Pages*. Learn more at eneidaescribe.com.

BARBARA ALVARADO holds an MA in literature and an MFA in poetry. She taught literature and writing for nearly 20 years before becoming a building inspector in 2022. She still writes and is currently interested in themes of labor. She resides in Texas.

PATRICK BARTON specializes in history and poetry. He is a former U.S. Army soldier who turned to academia after discharge.

CHELSEA BUNN is the author of *Forgiveness* (Finishing Line Press, 2019), finalist for the New Mexico/Arizona Book Award and the Eric Hoffer Book Award. The recipient of awards and grants from the Academy of American Poets, the Center for Women Writers, and New Mexico Writers, she is originally from New York City.

CLARE CHU hails from Palm Springs, California. She is an art curator, dealer, and lecturer who has authored numerous books on Asian art. Clare's collection of poetry, *The Sand Dune Teacher*, was published by UnCollected Press. Clare's recent chapbook, *Objects Heavy in This Life*, was published by Finishing Line Press.

DEVA EVELAND's work can be found in publications such as *Puerto del Sol*, *The Shanghai Literary Review*, and *New Dead Families*. He is the fiction editor for *Spittoon Monthly* and has also collaborated with the historian Hieronymus Atchley on *Oft Neglected Wars*, a compendium of strange and forgotten military conflicts.

AYOKUNLE FALOMO is Nigerian, American, and the author of *Autobiomythography of* (Alice James, 2024) and *AfricanAmerican't* (FlowerSong, 2022), among other titles. He has received fellowships from the Vermont Studio Center, MacDowell, and the University of Michigan's Helen Zell Writers' Program.

JAMIE TODD HAMILTON is a human being alive on planet Earth. Originally from Niagara Falls, Jamie graduated from Buffalo State University. Nomadic by nature, Jamie has lived in various cities along the Atlantic coast and is currently residing in Wheeling, West Virginia. Many people ask, "Why. Wheeling?" Jamie doesn't know . . . yet.

CHRIS HELGENS is a husband and father of five who enjoys writing short stories with his daughter, Morgan, from time to time. He is an avid movie fan, and when he's not busy mowing the lawn on his family's acreage in Iowa, you will probably find him watching a movie and munching on popcorn with his grandson or losing his retirement on the slot machines at the casino.

MYRLIN A. HERMES is the Lambda Award-winning author of *The Lunatic, the Lover, and the Poet* and *Careful What You Wish For*. Her novel about Aphra Behn, *Two Truths and a Lie*, was researched on a grant from the Arts Council England and is currently seeking a publisher.

JAHMAN HILL is an award-winning poet and playwright. In 2018, he claimed the title of third-best slam poet in the world. Jahman is a professor at the University of Alabama where he received master's degrees in both Communication Studies and Women's Studies.

GARETH HIPWELL is a Sydney-based Australian artist, freelance arts journalist, and author, writing for *Rolling Stone Australia*, *The Big Issue Australia*, *Australian Book Review*, and other publications. Gareth's short fiction has previously appeared in *Southerly*, *The Sleepers Almanac Vol. 9*, and *Seizure*. Gareth Instagrams regularly at @earthquakeinthepoorhouse.

AMANDA HODES is a writer and sound artist. She has an MA in creative writing from the University of East Anglia, and her poetry focuses on reparative writing, feminine performativity, and self-surveillance. Her work has been recognized by the Arts Club of Washington, Sound Scene Festival, Koster Foundation, and elsewhere.

D. SETH HORTON's fiction, poetry, essays, and scholarship have appeared in more than 60 publications. His latest book is a forthcoming collection of experimental stories set throughout the U.S.-Mexico borderlands entitled *On a NASA Flight to Heaven* (TCU Press, 2024). He teaches American literature at the University of Virginia.

MORGAN JEFFERY is a teacher of tough but lovable freshmen in Marion, Iowa. When she's not teaching writing or taking care of her two children, she tries her hand at writing stories of her own. Her work is published in *The Antigonish Review* and *Flash Fiction Magazine*.

JEREMY RAY JEWELL hails from Jacksonville, Florida. He has an MA in history of ideas from Birkbeck College, University of London, and a BA in philosophy from the University of Massachusetts Boston. He is a frequent contributor to Boston's *Arts Fuse* magazine. His website is jeremyrayjewell.com.

MARION AVRILYN JONES lives and writes in Coralville, Iowa.

P. D. R. LINDSAY makes New Zealand home. Born in Ireland and educated in England, Canada, and New Zealand, P. D. R. Lindsay writes historical stories about ordinary people whose names and lives we don't know much about. She finds that certain human traits can be better shown through historical stories than through contemporary ones.

CAITLIN MARIAH tries to capture the unsaid. From her published short in the 2019 edition of *Crack the Spine*'s anthology to her creative nonfiction, Caitlin explores the unheard. As graduate of Emerson College and a current student of Columbia's School of the Arts, her expeditions are far from over.

MARY JANE PANKE has poetry in various publications, including *Word Fountain*, *The Ekphrastic Review*, *Image Out Write*, *Poetry City*, *Whale Road Review*, *River River*, and *Fredericksburg Literary & Art Review*. She is a Pushcart and Best of the Net nominee and lives with her family near Hartford, Connecticut.

JONATHAN ANDREW PÉREZ is a lawyer, poet, and professor who is teaching at Wesleyan University an online course titled Poetic Justice: Race, Law, and Poetry in the 21st Century. He has been published in *Hayden's Ferry Review*, *Poetry Magazine*, *Split Lip*, *Guesthouse*, and *Rise Up Review*, among other outlets. Jonathan began his career as a community organizer.

ERIC PIERZCHALA is a humanities teacher and former professional baseball player, and he's taught chess to children for over a decade. Eric holds an MFA in poetry from Murray State University. His poems have most recently appeared in *Cathexis Northwest Press*, *Nonbinary Review*, *The Stirling Spoon*, *SurVision*, and the *Surrealists and Outsiders* anthology.

ESTHER RA is the author of *book of untranslatable things* (Grayson Books, 2018). She has been the recipient of numerous awards, including the Pushcart Prize, the 49th Parallel Award for Poetry, and the Women Writing War Poetry Award. Esther currently works to support healthcare for North Korean defectors in Seoul.

JOHANNAH RACZ KNUDSON's work has appeared in *Fourth Genre*, *Pithead Chapel*, *Sycamore Review*, *Puerto del Sol*, *Superstition Review*, and elsewhere. She lives with her husband in the shadow of the Rocky Mountains.

GREG RAPPLEYE's collection, *A Path between Houses* (University of Wisconsin Press, 2000), won the Brittingham Prize. His third book, *Figured Dark* (University of Arkansas Press, 2007), was cowinner of the Arkansas Prize in Poetry. His fourth collection is *Tropical Landscape with Ten Hummingbirds* (Dos Madres Press, 2018).

HENRY 7. RENEAU, JR. does not Twitter X, Facebook, LinkedIn, or Instagram. It is not that he is scared of change, or stuck fast in the past; instead, he has learned from experience: the crack pipe kills. He is the author of the poetry collection *freedomland blues* (Transcendent Zero Press) and the e-chapbook *physiography of the fittest* (Kind of a Hurricane Press).

GRETCHEN ROCKWELL is a queer poet whose work has appeared in *Agni, Cotton Xenomorph, Palette Poetry, Whale Road Review,* and elsewhere; xe has two chapbooks. Gretchen enjoys writing about gender, science, space, and unusual connections. Find xer at gretchenrockwell.com or on Twitter X and Instagram at @daft_rockwell.

DARYL SCROGGINS lives in Marfa, Texas. He is the author of *This Is Not the Way We Came In,* a collection of flash fiction and a flash novel (Ravenna Press). One of his fictions has been included in *Best Microfiction 2020.*

KATHRYN SMITH won the 2019-2020 Jake Adam York Prize for her second full-length collection, *Self-Portrait with Cephalopod,* which was published by Milkweed Editions. She is also the author of the full-length collection *Book of Exodus* (Scablands Books, 2017) and the chapbook *Chosen Companions of the Goblin* (Open Country Press, 2019).

J. W. STEWART is a graduate student at the University of North Texas, a teacher of 15 years, and an adjunct professor for Collin College. He has contributed several chapters to books on baseball history. He is an emerging writer of historical fiction.

STUART STROMIN is a South African-born writer and filmmaker, living in Los Angeles. He was educated at Rhodes University, South Africa, the Alliance française de Paris, and University of California, Los Angeles. His work has appeared in *Immigrant Report, Dissident Voice, Rigorous, The Raven,* and elsewhere. Find him at stuartstromin.com.

BOB SYKORA is the author of the forthcoming collection *Utopians in Love* (Game Over Books, 2025). A graduate of the UMass Boston MFA program, he teaches at a community college, edits with Garden Party Collective, cohosts *The Line Break* podcast, and curates the KC Poetry Calendar. Find him online at bobsykora.com.

ANIQUE SARA TAYLOR's *Civil Twilight* won the Blue Light Press 2022 Prize. *Where Space Bends* was published by Finishing Line Press, 2020. A Pushcart nominee, her books were chosen as a finalist by Harbor Review, Small Harbor, Minerva Rising, and Blue Light Press. She holds MFAs in poetry (Drew) and drawing (Pratt), a diplôme (Sorbonne), and a Master of Divinity.

LAURA BUDOFSKY WISNIEWSKI is the author of *Sanctuary, Vermont* (Orison Books), winner of the Orison Poetry Prize, the NEPC Book Prize, and a Foreword Indies Award. She is the author of *How to Prepare Bear* (Redbird Chapbooks). She won the Janet B. McCabe Poetry Prize and the *Poetry International* Prize and has work in *Narrative Magazine, The Missouri Review,* and elsewhere.

2019 Charter Oak Award

Alternating Current is dedicated to nurturing and promoting the independent press and its authors. We proudly honor our authors with annual writing awards, including the Charter Oak Award for Best Historical.

Legend has it that this unusually large white oak tree on what early colonists named Wyllys Hyll in Hartford, Connecticut, was where the Royal Charter of 1662 was shoved into a hidden hollow to thwart its confiscation by the English governor-general who wished to revoke the piece of legislation that granted autonomy to the colonists. This tree, named the Charter Oak, has since become a symbol of the power of documents and recorded history, the freedom they give us, showcasing the lengths one would go to protect, to defend, and to stand by words that could forever change the course of people's lives. While the Charter Oak is a strong, undeniable piece of American history, its symbol is universal. Words empower us all, the whole world over, and we'll die to protect our collective right to them. Alternating Current wants to preserve and reward those words that empower us, so that they, too, may go down in history.

The Charter Oak Award for Best Historical is awarded annually to a single piece of work that is historical in nature. The winning piece receives print publication in *Footnote*; online publication in our journal *The Coil*; online listings on our website; complimentary copies of the *Footnote* print journal featuring the winning piece indicated with our medallion imprint; a certificate; a cash honorarium; and our virtual medallion with permission for use on the author's websites and any published books or online outlets. A second and a third place and nine finalists receive print publication in *Footnote*; publication on *The Coil*; and other prizes. Full details can be found at our website. The winners are announced each year with the annual release of *Footnote*. The 2019 judging process consisted of submissions being sent incognito to the history editors, where the finalists and top pieces were determined.

Acknowledgments

 Special acknowledgment to Devin Byrnes and SuA Kang at Hardly Square, for their creativity in designing our Charter Oak Award medallion imprint.

Hardly Square is a strategy, branding, and design-based boutique located in Baltimore, Maryland, that specializes in graphic design, web design, and eLearning courses. Their invaluable expertise has made our annual awards come to life.

Alternating Current Press wishes to acknowledge the following publications where pieces from this issue first appeared:

"The Birthday Party, 1944" was previously published in *The Sand Dune Teacher.*

"The Girl from No Gun Ri" was previously published on *The Rumpus.*

"selective recall" was previously published in *Upstairs in the Library, Hardpan: A Journal of Poetry, Blue Moon Literary & Art Review, Tic Toc, Storm Cycle 2014: The Best of Kind of a Hurricane Press,* and *Rise Up Review.*

"For Samuel Ajayi Crowther" was previously published in *African, American.*

"After the Hostile Takeover, 1990" was previously published in *Sanctuary, Vermont.*

"Considering 'the Public Appears Disposed to Being Amused Even When They Are Conscious of Being Deceived' (P. T. Barnum, 1855)," "The Fox Sisters Hold a Séance," "Maggie Fox Speaks to the Dead Girl, Then Is Asked to Remove Her Clothes," "The Examination," and "Animal Magnetism vs. Spiritual Magnetism, or the Vertiginous Sister Attempts a Mesmeric State in Order to More Fully Understand" were previously published in *Chosen Companions of the Goblin.*

Bibliographies & Endnotes

"Army without a Country" borrows its title from the book *The Army without a Country* by Edwin P. Hoyt.

"The Untold Story of the 2nd North Carolina Mounted Infantry" cites the following references that correspond to the numbers within the text: [1] 2nd North Carolina Mounted Infantry. *2nd and 3rd North Carolina Mounted Infantry Regimental Rosters.* 2ncmi.org/2-3rosters.html. [2] American Civil War. thomaslegion .net. [3] American Civil War. *Thomas' Legion.* thomaslegion.net/2ndnorth carolinamountedinfantryregiment.html. [4] Collins, Donald, E. *Union Volunteer Regiments.* Encyclopedia of North Carolina (University of North Carolina Press, 2006). ncpedia.org/union-volunteer-regiments. [5] Foner, Eric. *Forever Free: The Story of Emancipation and Reconstruction.* (New York: Vintage Books, 2005). 11. [6] Freehling, William. *The South vs. The South: How Anti-Confederate Southerners Shaped the Course of the Civil War.* (New York: Oxford University Press, 2001). 40-42. [7] Hartley, Chris J. *Stoneman's 1865 Raid.* (Winston-Salem: John F. Blair, 2010). essentialcivilwarcurriculum.com/stonemans-1865-raid.html. [8] Inscoe, John C. *Race, War, and Remembrance in the Appalachian South.* (Lexington: University Press of Kentucky, 2008). 0-www.jstor.org. library.acaweb.org/stable/j.ctt2jct8v.17. [9] Inscoe, John, and McKinney, Gordon. *The Heart of Confederate Appalachia: Western North Carolina in the Civil War.* (Durham: University of North Carolina Press, 2000). 250. [10] Leigh, Penny. *Hendersonville Times-News.* Hendersonville, North Carolina. January 1, 2000. [11] National Park Service. *The Civil War.* nps.gov/civilwar/search-battle-units-detail.htm?battleUnitCode=UTN0002RI. [12] North Carolina Department of Cultural Resources. *George W. Kirk Biography.* NCDCR Office of Archives and History. 2011. civilwarexperience.ncdcr.gov/biographies/kirk.htm [removed]. [13] Stephens, Alexander. "Corner Stone" Speech. Savannah, Georgia. March 21, 1861. [14] *The Western Democrat.* (Charlotte, NC), April 5, 1864. *Chronicling America: Historic American Newspapers.* Lib. of Congress. chroniclingamerica.loc .gov/lccn/sn84020712/1864-04-05/ed-1/seq-1. [15] *The Western Democrat.* (Charlotte, NC), March 21, 1865. *Chronicling America: Historic American Newspapers.* Lib. of Congress. chroniclingamerica.loc.gov/lccn/sn84020712/1865-03-21/ed-1/seq-3. [16] *The Western Democrat.* (Charlotte, NC), August 23, 1864. *Chronicling America: Historic American Newspapers.* Lib. of Congress. chronicling america.loc.gov/lccn/sn84020712/1864-08-23/ed-1/seq-1. [17] *The Western Democrat.* (Charlotte, NC), September 26, 1865. *Chronicling America: Historic American Newspapers.* Lib. of Congress. chroniclingamerica.loc.gov/lccn/ sn84020712/1865-09-26/ed-1/seq-2. [18] Trotter, William. *Bushwhackers: The Civil War in North Carolina: The Mountains.* (John F. Blair, 1988). 11, 33.

"Georgetown Girls" author's note: In Spring 2018, I took a course at Harvard University with Professor John Stauffer to examine the Civil War era through the analysis of literature, including work by Frederick Douglass, W. E. B. Du Bois, and Mark Twain. Throughout the course, I wondered how a society at war with itself affected children, specifically young girls. I found few examples in the literature covered by the course, either because the female characters were one-dimensional or because they were relegated to the background. I yearned to see the Civil War era through a girl's perspective—one raised closer to the North, exposed to abolitionism. This desire inspired me to write "Georgetown Girls" for the final course project. "Georgetown Girls" portrays the experiences of characters who could have been real people to offer a critique of Civil War society and to hold open a window to the past for modern readers. As I learned in the course, we must bear witness to history, even when it is difficult, in order to come closer to the truth. Only then are we able to understand the present, an essential step toward enacting change. In addition to the required texts of the course—such as Drew Faust's *The Republic of Suffering*, Harriet Beecher Stowe's *Uncle Tom's Cabin*, and David Blight's *Race and Reunion: The Civil War in American Memory*—I relied on several other sources to craft this story. The list includes Joseph Dorst Patch's *The Battle of Ball's Bluff*, Susan C. Lawrence's *Civil War Washington*, Jennifer Lynn Altenhofel's "Keeping House: Irish and Irish-American Women in the District of Columbia, 1850-1890," the U.S. National Library of Medicine Digital Collections, Mary A. Mitchell's "An Intimate Journey through Georgetown in April 1863," and Canden Schwantes' *Wicked Georgetown: Scoundrels, Sinners, and Spies*.

"No Locks" is imagined based on an event described in Everett Webber's *Escape to Utopia: The Communal Movement in America* (1959).

"At New Lebanon They Danced like Ghosts" borrows and draws from language found in a firsthand account of Shaker prayer described in an article of the same name published in *The Harbinger*, Volume 5 (J. S. Dwight, August 14, 1847), and *Gleanings from Old Shaker Journals* (Clara Endicott Sears, 1916).

"The Hummingbird Artist Dreams of the Ladder of Heaven" author notes: The 1863-1864 journey to Brazil made by American painter Martin Johnson Heade (1819-1905) to paint hummingbirds is a matter of record, and I have looked to the work of Professor Theodore Stebbins, Jr., for certain details regarding that trip, Heade's work, and the artist's aesthetic approach to what he found in that country. Stebbins' works used for reference were: *Martin Johnson Heade* (Yale University Press, 1999) and *The Life and Work of Martin Johnson Heade: A Critical Analysis and Catalog Raisonné* (Yale University Press, 2000). Though reference is occasionally made in my poems to the notebooks of Martin Johnson Heade, I did not rely upon the actual notebooks (except for a few excerpts found in the work of Professor Stebbins) in composing this or any of the other poems in my collection from which this piece comes, *Tropical Landscape with Ten Hummingbirds* (Dos Madres Press, 2018). While attentive to dates and certain facts, I have freely imagined Heade's personality, feelings, and response to historic events. Heade is often grouped with the Hudson River School of American painters, and he was a close associate of Frederic Edwin Church. The exact contents and order of appearance Heade intended for the *Gems of Brazil* series, the unpublished volume that was to feature his hummingbird paintings, is unknown. Much of what experts believe was meant for inclusion in the bound volume of lithographs can be found in the Manoogian Collection, which is in private hands in Michigan. Sixteen of Heade's hummingbird paintings are in the permanent collection of the Crystal Bridge Museum of American Art in Bentonville, Arkansas. Other examples of Heade's work appear in museums and art collections across the United States and Europe. The inscriptions on the golden steps in "The Hummingbird Artist Dreams of the Ladder of Heaven" are suggested by *The Ladder of Divine Ascent* (c. 600 CE), a monastic treatise by St. John Climacus.

Colophon & Permissions

The edition you are holding is the First Print Edition pressing of this publication.

Footnote logo set in Alternating Current-created font. Subfont on cover set in Old Newspaper Types, created by Manfred Klein. Back cover Alternating Current Press font set in Portmanteau, created by JLH Fonts. Number "5" on title pages set in 1942 Report, created by Johan Holmdahl. Interior title font set in 1550, created by Frédéric Michaud. Image captions set in Avenir Book, created by Adrian Frutiger. Place markers for Charter Oak Award set in Alcubierre, created by Matt Ellis. All other fonts set in Iowan Old Style, created by John Downer, inspired by typefaces from Renaissance Italy, with influence from Downer's work as a hand-painter of signs.

Cover artwork designed by Leah Angstman using images by Dorothe from Darkmoon Art, Jean-Pierre Pellissier, and Gordon Johnson. Alternating Current lightbulb logo created by Leah Angstman, ©2006, 2023 Alternating Current. Charter Oak Award medallion created by SuA Kang and Devin Byrnes of Hardly Square, for Alternating Current's sole use. Hardly Square logo © 2023 Hardly Square. Charter Oak silhouette courtesy Clker.

creativecommons.org/licenses/by-sa/3.0/deed.en; photo corners rounded. (45) Indonesian comfort women photo PD-US. (46) Korean comfort girls photo PD-US work prepared by a U.S. Army officer during official duty, under terms of TITLE 17, CHAPTER 1, SECTION 105 of U.S. Code, courtesy U.S. National Archives, SC-262580. (46) Chinese and Malayan comfort girls photo by Sergeant A. E. Lemon of British NO. 9 Army Film & Photographic Unit; reproduced scan PD-US work taken prior to June 1, 1957, in accordance with HMSO's declaration of expiry of Crown Copyrights worldwide, courtesy Imperial War Museum. (53) Korean refugees photo PD-US work prepared by an officer or official of the U.S. government during official duty, under terms of TITLE 17, CHAPTER 1, SECTION 105 of U.S. Code, courtesy U.S. Defense Department. (54) Muccio memo PD-US work prepared by an officer or official of the U.S. government during official duty, under terms of TITLE 17, CHAPTER 1, SECTION 105 of U.S. Code, courtesy U.S. National Archives and Records Administration. (54) Bullet holes photo by Amlou2518, under Creative Commons Attribution-Share Alike 4.0 International license; photo corners rounded. (55) Bridge at No Gun Ri photo courtesy No Gun Ri International Peace Foundation, under Creative Commons Attribution-Share Alike 3.0 Unported license; photo corners rounded. (55) Rogers memo PD-US work prepared by a U.S. Air Force airman or employee during official duty, under terms of TITLE 17, CHAPTER 1, SECTION 105 of U.S. Code, courtesy U.S. National Archives and Records Administration. (58) All-Star Bowling Lane photo by Ammodramus, under Creative Commons 1.0 Universal Public Domain Dedication. (59) Orangeburg massacre photo licensed for editorial and commercial use by Getty Images. (59) Delano Middleton, Samuel Hammond, Jr., and Henry Smith photos widely available online, used in low-resolution under educational fair use. (61) FBI missing-persons poster PD-US work prepared by an FBI employee during official duty. (62) Chaney, Goodman, and Schwerner burial photo PD-US work prepared by an officer or employee of the U.S. government during official duty, courtesy Public Broadcasting Service. (62) Mt. Zion history marker photo by Rob Ferguson, Jr., under Creative Commons Attribution-Share Alike 3.0 Unported license; photo corners rounded, righthand side cropped. (69) Sanitation workers photo by Richard L. Copley, PD-US courtesy Learning for Justice. (79) Bekkersdal mounted police photo by Wesley Fester, under Creative Commons Attribution 2.0 Generic license, creativecommons.org/licenses/by/2.0/deed.en; photo corners rounded, contrast lightened for better printing. (79) Barefoot police photo PD-US. (85) Freetown painting PD-US courtesy Colonial Williamsburg Foundation; and United Nations Educational, Scientific, and Cultural Organization. (103) Florida Civil War illustration PD-US courtesy Florida Memory: State Library and Archives of Florida, reference collection number RC11533. (119) Cherokee Confederates photo PD-US courtesy thomaslegion.net. (119) George Kirk photo PD-US courtesy Ancestry.com and OvertAnalyzer. (139) *The Battle of Ball's Bluff, VA: Rescuing the Body of Brig. Gen. Baker* [NB: erroneously called "Brig. Gen." Baker turned down the position of brigadier general and chose instead to be a colonel] illustration by F. O. C. Darley and J. Godfrey from *The Great Civil War, Vol. I* by

Robt. Towes, M.D., and Benjamin G. Smith (New York: Virtue & Yorston, 1865), PD-US courtesy Missouri Historical Society, identifier P0084-0616, reference number 157641, under MHS Open-Access Policy. (139) *Retreat of the Federalists after the Fight at Ball's Bluff, Upper Potomac, Virginia* engraving from *The Illustrated London News*, November 23, 1861, p. 514, PD-US courtesy Library of Congress Prints and Photographs division, digital ID CPH.3B45878. (141) Edward Baker photo by E. & H. T. Anthony PD-US courtesy Library of Congress Prints and Photographs division, digital ID PPMSCA.08348. (142) Mary Edwards Walker photo PD-US courtesy U.S. Department of Health and Human Services and the National Institutes of Health. (146) Washington Arsenal monument PD-US courtesy Historic American Landscapes Survey division of National Park Service, accession number HALS DC-1-7; and Library of Congress Prints and Photographs division, digital ID DC1018.PHOTOS. 200691P. (147) Washington Arsenal women photo PD-US courtesy Library of Congress Prints and Photographs division and Joint Base Myer-Henderson Hall. (147) Washington Arsenal destruction photo PD-US courtesy National Defense University Library Special Collections. (148) Maria Anna Mozart painting PD-US. (150) *The Virgin and Unicorn* fresco by Domenichino PD-US courtesy Palazzo Farnese; photo by Mauro Magliani, copyrighted and licensed for editorial use by Aliani Archives/ Corbis Images, under control of Getty Images, used with editorial permission. (150) *The Lady and the Unicorn (La dama e l'unicorno)* painting by Luca Longhi PD-US courtesy Museo Nazionale di Castel Sant'Angelo, accession number INV. 51/III STANZA DI PAOLO III. (151) *The Unicorn Surrenders to a Maiden* (from the *Unicorn Tapestries*) tapestry PD-US courtesy Met Cloisters, a gift of John D. Rockefeller, Jr., 1938, accession number 38.51.2, under Metropolitan Museum of Art Open Access Policy. (151) *The Lady and the Unicorn: Sight (Tapestry Cycle)* PD-US courtesy Evening.star. (158) Russian laborers photo by Lewis Hine PD-US courtesy Miriam and Ira D. Wallach Division of Art, Prints, and Photographs: Photography Collection, New York Public Library Digital Collections, UUID C312A980-C608-012F-9F5C-58D385A7BC34. (159) Russian woman with needlework photo by Andreï Osipovich Karelin PD-US courtesy Miriam and Ira D. Wallach Division of Art, Prints, and Photographs: Photography Collection, New York Public Library Digital Collections, UUID B2ED8310-C6BB-012F-B396-58D385A7BC34. (159) Russian woman with house interior photo by Andreï Osipovich Karelin PD-US courtesy Miriam and Ira D. Wallach Division of Art, Prints, and Photographs: Photography Collection, New York Public Library Digital Collections, UUID B4F85D10-C62C-012F-E0DE-58D385A7BC34. (159) Russian woman sitting in chair photo PD-US from *Zhanochy Kastsyum na Belarusi* by V. M. Byalyavina and L. V. Rakava (Minsk: Belarus Publ., 2007), p. 350, courtesy Pracar. (162) Felix the Cat photo PD-US courtesy *Ominous Octopus Omnibus*. (165) Henry David Thoreau etching of photo by Geo. F. Parlow PD-US work prepared by an officer or official of the U.S. government during official duty, under terms of TITLE 17, CHAPTER 1, SECTION 105 of U.S. Code, courtesy Library of Congress, loc.gov/item/ 95513963, with digital distortion corrected by Sealle. (171) *The Rover* photo by Eric Polk, under Creative Commons Attribution-Share Alike 4.0 International license;

photo corners rounded. (172) Aphra Behn engraving of John Riley's lost portrait PD-US courtesy Gabriel VanHelsing, under Creative Commons CC0 1.0 Universal Public Domain Dedication license. (183) Lavender Scare headline and protest photo courtesy *The Lavender Scare*, thelavenderscare.com/epk. (186) Ducking engraving PD-US courtesy Wethersfield Historical Society. (192) Kathryn Smith photo by Dean Davis, copyrighted 2023, used with permission. (194) Faiber and Barnum photo PD-US courtesy National Portrait Gallery, Smithsonian Institution, Frederick Hill Meserve Collection, object number NPG.81.M218, under Creative Commons CC0 1.0 Universal Public Domain Dedication license; digitized with better contrast by Daderot, under Creative Commons CC0 1.0 Universal Public Domain Dedication license. (194) P. T. Barnum photo by Landy PD-US courtesy Harvard University, Houghton Library, Harvard Theater Collection, HOLLIS number OLVWORK606437, under Harvard's open access policy for public domain images; cropped with higher contrast by Scewing. (196) *Mrs. Fish and the Misses Fox: The Original Mediums of the Mysterious Noises at Rochester Western, N.Y.* lithograph after a daguerreotype by Richard B. Appleby, from N. Currier (New York: Currier & Ives, c. 1852), PD-US courtesy Library of Congress Prints and Photographs division, LCCN 2002710596. (199) Shoe tips photo by John Elfreth Watkins, Jr., from "In the Land of Spooks with the Spirit Fakers," *The Philadelphia Record*, September 22, 1907, PD-US courtesy Lone Wolfs. (199) Eusapia freeing her hand photo montage PD-US from *Mysterious Psychic Forces: An Account of the Author's Investigations in Psychical Research, Together with Those of Other European Savants* by Camille Flammarion (Boston: Small, Maynard, and Company, 1907), courtesy Internet Archive Book Images under Flickr's The Common license. (202) *Kate and Maggie Fox, Spirit Mediums from Rochester, New York* daguerreotype by Thomas M. Easterly PD-US courtesy Missouri Historical Society, identifier N17196, under MHS Open-Access Policy. (202) *Medium* glass negative by George Grantham Bain PD-US courtesy Library of Congress Prints and Photographs division and George Grantham Bain Collection, which asserts no copyright restrictions for use, loc.gov/rr/print/res/274_bain.html, reproduction number LC-DIG-GGBAIN-03135 DLC, LCCN 2014683129. (205) *Photo of Sir Arthur Conan Doyle with Spirit* photo by Ada Deane PD-US courtesy Pdhero37. (206) *Geest van sir Arthur Conan Doyle (The Ghost of Sir Arthur Conan Doyle)* photo by William Hope courtesy Nationaal Archief of Netherlands, Spaarnestad Photo, and *Het Leven*, under Flickr's The Common license. (207) William Hope photo PD-US due to copyright elapse, from *Index to Psychic Science: An Introduction to Systematized Knowledge of Psychical Experience* by S. R. Morgan (Swarthmore, Pennsylvania: Swarthmore, 1950), courtesy HealthyGirl. (207) Tweedale spirit photo PD-US courtesy Cloudy Apple. (208) Nashoba illustration PD-US from *Domestic Manners of the Americans* by Frances Milton Trollope (London: Whittaker, Treacher, & Co., 1832), courtesy Tennessee State Library and Archives. (210) *Shakers' Dance* illustration by Benson John Lossing PD-US courtesy New York Public Library Digital Collections, Jerome Robbins Dance Division, image ID 5372700. (210) *Shakers* illustration by Arthur Boyd Houghton PD-US courtesy New York Public Library Digital Collections, Jerome Robbins Dance Division, image ID 5372699. (213) *Passion Flowers and Hummingbirds* by Martin Johnson Heade PD-US courtesy Museum of Fine Arts Boston, a gift of Maxim Karolik for the M. and M. Karolik Collection of American Paintings 1815–1865. (213) Martin Johnson Heade photo PD-US. (214) *Two Hummingbirds with Their Young* by Martin Johnson Heade PD-US courtesy Yale University Art Gallery, a gift of Jerald Dillon Fessenden, accession number 2011.127.1, under Creative Commons CC0 1.0 Universal Public Domain Dedication license. (224) Man with a dog head from *The Nuremberg Chronicle* by Hartmann Schedel, illustrated by Michael Wolmegut (Nuremberg: Anton Koberger for Sebald Schreyer and Sebastian Kammermeister, 1493), PD-US courtesy Bavarian State Library and U.S. Library of Congress, LCCN 2021666735. (227) Lawrence Washington unattributed line engraving reproduction of c. 1738 portrait attributed to Gustavus Hesselius, PD-US courtesy Mount Vernon Ladies' Association and Granger Historical Picture Archive. (242) *Days Gone By* photo by Jo of Wandering Soles Photography, under Creative Commons Attribution 2.0 Generic license; photo corners rounded.

Text permissions and licenses: (63) "A Confession of Conspiracy" text is a released PD-US public FBI record, courtesy National Archives and Records Administration. (82) "How I Was Captured into Slavery" text PD-US from *A Patriot to the Core: Bishop Ajayi Crowther*, J. F. Ade-Ajayi (Ibadan, Nigeria: Anglican Diocese of Ibadan, 1992), courtesy "Ajayi Crowther's 179-year-old letter: My capture into slavery and rescue," *The Nigeria News*, June 25, 2016, thenewsnigeria.com.ng/2016/06/25/ajayi-crowthers-179-year-old-letter-my-capture-into-slavery-and-rescue. (140) "Death of Colonel Baker" lyrics PD-US courtesy Library of Congress, Rare Books and Special Collections division, *America Singing: Nineteenth-Century Song Sheets*, digital ID AMSS.CW101290. (164) "Sympathy" text PD-US courtesy Henry David Thoreau Online. (172) "The Dream" text PD-US courtesy Poetry Foundation. (187) "The Case of Grace Sherwood" text PD-US from *Narratives of the Witchcraft Cases, 1648-1706* by George Lincoln Burr, ed. (New York: Charles Scribner's Sons, 1914), p. 438-442, courtesy *Encyclopedia Virginia*, Virginia Humanities. (203) "An Excerpt from *The History of Spiritualism*" text from *The History of Spiritualism, Vol. I* by Arthur Conan Doyle (New York: George H. Duran, 1926), PD-US courtesy Project Gutenberg Australia.

General permissions and licenses: Any work prepared by an officer or employee of the U.S. Government as part of that person's official duties is PD-US and no protection can be claimed via copyright law; this includes works of government departments, divisions, military, and NPS. All other images and non-contemporary materials PD-US without attribution necessary or with attribution unknown. All fonts, artwork, graphics, and designs were used with permission. All rights reserved.

Other Works from
Alternating Current Press

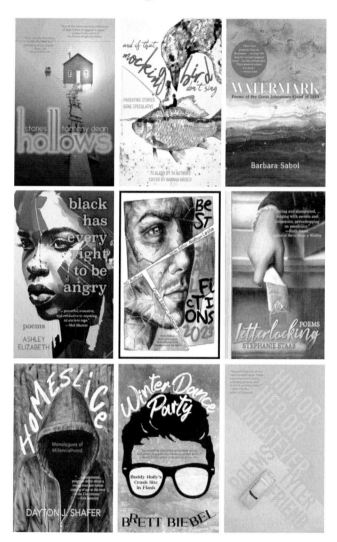

altcurrentpress.com

Made in United States
North Haven, CT
06 January 2024

47106515R00162